FIRST COURSE IN
THEORY OF NUMBERS

FIRST COURSE IN
THEORY OF NUMBERS

BY

HARRY N. WRIGHT

Associate Professor of Mathematics
The City College, New York

NEW YORK

JOHN WILEY & SONS, Inc.

London: CHAPMAN & HALL, Limited

1939

PRINTED IN U. S. A.

PRESS OF
BRAUNWORTH & CO., INC.
BUILDERS OF BOOKS
BRIDGEPORT, CONN.

PREFACE

This book is written to serve as a textbook for a one-semester course in the theory of numbers. Much care has been taken to make it relatively easy reading for the student, and at the same time to see that the reasoning is complete and accurate. A large number of exercises is provided. The arrangement of text and exercises is made to meet the requirements of classroom use. In the process of preparation the book has been used in classes at City College, New York, by both Professor Bennington P. Gill and the author. During its writing and its experimental use the author has had the privilege of frequent conferences with Professor Gill, who has given generously of his time in criticism and in editorial assistance. Much credit is due to him for the results attained.

The choice of subject matter for the course is largely determined by general usage and probably does not vary much among the colleges of the country. There may be some lack of agreement with the emphasis placed upon certain topics. For example, some would probably give less time to continued fractions than is called for in Chapter II, or possibly some would omit the section on the Jacobi symbol in Chapter IV. We feel that the length of Chapter II is justified by the fact that in this discussion of the simple continued fraction we have presented a well-rounded and interesting unit of the subject. Moreover, this discussion serves well to give the student valuable experience in algebraic reasoning without at the same time introducing too many new concepts. The consideration of the equation $x^2 - Dy^2 = N$ could have been postponed to Chapter V; but, since this treatment of it is so intimately related to the continued fraction theory, the presentation along with that theory seems more effective. As to the Jacobi symbol, it is an important tool for later use in number theory and is very naturally introduced along with the discussion of the Legendre symbol in Chapter IV.

Power residues and indices are used rather extensively in the

v

53214

latter part of the chapter on congruences. They make possible relatively simple and interesting solutions of certain problems and form a natural introduction to the chapter on quadratic residues.

The text contains sufficient material so that omissions may be made from one or more of Chapters II, IV, and V, and still there will remain a full semester's course for many undergraduate classes.

H. N. WRIGHT

September 6, 1939

CONTENTS

vii

ERRATA

Page 13, line 18: $\dfrac{n}{\pi p_i}$ should be $\dfrac{n}{\pi d_i}$.

Page 19, Ex. 12: Add "where $x > 1$ and is not necessarily an integer."

Page 27: After line 9 insert "in which by page 16 we make n even or odd

according as $\dfrac{p_n}{q_n} - x$ is $>$ or < 0."

In line 14 lower all $+$ signs except the first.

Page 49: The last clause of Ex. 9 should read "and use Euler's generalization of Fermat's Theorem."

Page 58: "Theorem 3" in line 16 should be "Theorem 7."

Page 64, in second line of Lemma: Insert "incongruent" before "numbers."

Page 67, lines 16, 17, and 18: Replace n by h.

Page 68, lines 6 and 8: Replace "$r^{(p-1)}\,p^{n-2}$" by "$r^{(p-1)p^{n-2}}$."

Page 98, line 22: Replace "$Am^2 - n^2$" and "$Am^2 + n^2$" by "$rm^2 - sn^2$" and "$rm^2 + sn^2$," respectively.

line 4: After "solutions" insert "(all listed as positive)."

FIRST COURSE IN THEORY OF NUMBERS

Chapter I

DIVISIBILITY

1. Definitions. The numbers which will be of principal interest in this study are the positive integers. However, unless otherwise limited, the term integer is used to include negative integers and zero. *Letters throughout our work will be understood to denote integers except when otherwise defined.*

We assume without discussion that the operations addition, subtraction, and multiplication when applied to integers yield integers. Also it is assumed that these operations obey the usual laws of commutation, association, and distribution.

When $a \cdot b = c$, where, in accordance with our notational agreement above, a, b, and c are integers, we say that a and b are *divisors* or *factors* of c, and that c *is divisible by*, or is a *multiple* of, a and also of b. That is, in $5 \cdot 13 = 65$, 5 and 13 are divisors of 65, and 65 is divisible by, or is a multiple of, 5 and also of 13. In particular, by writing $a \cdot 1 = a$, attention is called to the obvious fact that each integer is divisible by itself and unity. Such divisibility by unity will not usually require explicit mention.

If an integer $p > 1$ has no divisors other than $\pm p$ and ± 1 it is called a *prime*; if it has other divisors it is said to be *composite*. The primes <20 are 2, 3, 5, 7, 11, 13, 17, 19. Integers are called *even* or *odd* according as they are or are not divisible by 2; from which it follows that all primes other than 2 are odd. Then an even integer may always be represented by the form $2n$ and an odd integer by either of the forms $2n + 1$ or $2n - 1$. Two integers which are both even or both odd are said to have the *same parity*; if one is even and the other odd they have *different parity*.

If $m = a \cdot b$ and $n = a \cdot c$, a is said to be a *common* divisor of m and n. Then, since

$$m \pm n = ab \pm ac = a(b \pm c)$$

it follows that the sum or the difference of two integers is divisible by any common divisor of them. In particular we note that the sum or the difference of two integers having the same parity is even; for

$$2m \pm 2n = 2(m \pm n) = 2k$$

and $(2m + 1) \pm (2n + 1) = 2(m + n + 1)$ or $2(m - n)$

Likewise, since $(2m + 1) \pm 2n = 2(m \pm n) + 1$

the sum or difference of two integers having unlike parity is odd.

2. Greatest common divisor. The largest positive integer which divides the absolute values of each of two integers is called their *greatest common divisor*, abbreviated g.c.d. Given two positive integers m and n, their g.c.d. may be found by the following method, known as the Euclidean algorithm. Assume $m > n$, and divide m by n, getting the quotient q_1, and the remainder r_1. Here $q_1 = \left[\dfrac{m}{n}\right]$ $\left(\text{this being the symbolic way of writing that } q_1 \text{ is the } \textit{greatest integer} \text{ in } \dfrac{m}{n}\right)$, and we have the inequality $0 \leqq r_1 < n$. Then similarly divide n by r_1, getting $q_2 = \left[\dfrac{n}{r_1}\right]$ and r_2, where $0 \leqq r_2 < r_1$. The divisions may be continued thus

$$m = nq_1 + r_1$$

$$n = r_1q_2 + r_2$$

$$r_1 = r_2q_3 + r_3$$

$$\cdot \quad \cdot \quad \cdot \quad \cdot \quad \cdot \quad \cdot$$

$$r_{i-1} = r_iq_{i+1} + r_{i+1}$$

$$\cdot \quad \cdot \quad \cdot \quad \cdot \quad \cdot \quad \cdot$$

until the remainder, which is positive and decreasing with each step, becomes zero, which it must do in a finite number of steps, for there is only a finite number of non-negative integers less than a given integer. If this number of steps is $k + 1$, the last division is written

$$r_{k-1} = r_kq_{k+1}$$

It follows that r_k is a divisor of r_{k-1}. Then, from the preceding equation $r_{k-2} = r_{k-1}q_k + r_k$, it follows that r_k, being a divisor of each term of the right member, is a divisor of their sum r_{k-2}.

Carrying the argument back step by step, r_k is seen to be a divisor of each r_i and finally of m and of n.

On the other hand, writing the first equation $m - nq_1 = r_1$, any common divisor of m and n is seen to be also a divisor of r_1. From the second equation it is seen to be a divisor of r_2 and from succeeding equations of each r_i, and finally of r_k.

Then since we have seen that r_k is a common divisor of m and n, and, conversely, that any common divisor of m and n must also divide r_k, it follows that r_k is the greatest common divisor of m and n. This is written $(m, n) = r_k$. In particular, if $r_k = 1$, m and n are said to be *relatively prime*, or *prime to each other*.

Example. Find the g.c.d. of 7469 and 2387. We write

$$7469 = 2387 \cdot 3 + 308$$
$$2387 = 308 \cdot 7 + 231$$
$$308 = 231 \cdot 1 + 77$$
$$231 = 77 \cdot 3$$

Therefore $(7469, 2387) = 77$.

EXERCISES I

By the Euclidean algorithm find the g.c.d. of:

1. 5320 and 4389. **2.** 4147 and 10,672. **3.** 8749 and 11,143.

4. Show that, if n is odd, $n(n^2 - 1)$ is divisible by 24.

5. Find the highest power of 3 which is contained in $\lfloor 100$ (factorial 100; that is, $1 \cdot 2 \cdot 3 \cdots 99 \cdot 100$; 100! is also used with the same meaning).

6. Show that the square of an odd number is of the form $8n + 1$.

7. Show that $x^2 + y^2 = z^2$ cannot be true in integers when both x and y are odd.

8. Show that $n^5 - n$ is divisible by 30.

9. Show that, if $2^n - 1$ is a prime, n is a prime. *Suggestion*: Use the algebraic factors of $a^n - 1$.

10. Show that, if $2^n + 1$ is a prime, n is a power of 2.

11. Show that, if p is a prime > 3, $p = 6n \pm 1$.

12. For what set of least positive values of b will the forms $4n + b$ include all odd primes? For what set of numerically least values of b? The same questions for the forms $12n + b$ to include all primes > 3?

3. Properties of the g.c.d. THEOREM 1. *If* $(m, n) = d$, *where* $m = m'd$ *and* $n = n'd$, *then* $(m', n') = 1$.

For, if m' and n' had a common divisor $d' > 1$, dd' would divide both m and n, and d could not be their greatest common divisor.

4 DIVISIBILITY

THEOREM 2. *The greatest common divisor of two positive integers may be expressed as a linear homogeneous function of them with integral coefficients.*

To prove this we note that r_k, the g.c.d. of m and n as found above, is the last remainder >0 and occurs in the equation

$$r_{k-2} = r_{k-1}q_k + r_k$$

from which $\qquad r_k = r_{k-2} - r_{k-1}q_k$

Similarly, from the previous equation,

$$r_{k-1} = r_{k-3} - r_{k-2}q_{k-1}$$

Substituting this value of r_{k-1} in the expression for r_k, we get

$$r_k = r_{k-2}(1 + q_{k-1}q_k) - r_{k-3}q_k$$

a linear homogeneous function of r_{k-2} and r_{k-3} with integral coefficients. Continuing with similar substitutions of the values of $r_{k-2}, r_{k-3}, \cdots, r_1$ in turn, r_k is finally expressed as a function of m and n. Since the expression for each r_i as substituted is homogeneous and linear in r_{i-1} and r_{i-2} and has integral coefficients, these characteristics of the expression for r_k are preserved, and

$$r_k = mA + nB$$

where A and B are integers (not necessarily positive).

From the illustrative example of the g.c.d. used above

$$77 = 308 - 231$$
$$= 308 \cdot 8 - 2387$$
$$= 7469 \cdot 8 - 2387 \cdot 25$$

COROLLARY. *If* $(m, n) = 1$, *integers* A *and* B *can be found such that* $mA + nB = 1$.

This follows as a special case of the theorem when the g.c.d. of m and n is unity.

THEOREM 3. *If* $(m, n) = 1$, *any common divisor of* m *and* nk *is a divisor of* k.

For, since $(m, n) = 1$,

$$mA + nB = 1$$

and $\qquad mkA + nkB = k$

Then any divisor of m and nk divides the left member of the equation and hence divides k.

COROLLARY 1. *If* $(m, n) = 1$ *and* $(m, k) = 1$, *then* $(m, nk) = 1$. For, if $(m, nk) = d > 1$, by the theorem d would divide both m and k, contrary to $(m, k) = 1$.

COROLLARY 2. *If each of any number of integers is prime to* m, *their product is prime to* m.

4. Solution of the Diophantine * equation $ax + by = c$. Theorem 2 is useful in finding integral solutions x, y of the indeterminate equation

(1) $$ax + by = c$$

in which a, b, and c are given integers. We first note that, if $(a, b) = d > 1$, d is a divisor of $ax + by$ and therefore must divide c if x and y are to be integers. Then if d does not divide c the solution of (1) in integers is impossible.

Assuming that d is a divisor of c, we divide (1) through by d and get

(2) $$\frac{a}{d}x + \frac{b}{d}y = \frac{c}{d}$$

in which $\frac{a}{d}, \frac{b}{d}$, and $\frac{c}{d}$ are integers, and, by Theorem 1, $\left(\frac{a}{d}, \frac{b}{d}\right) = 1$. Clearly, integral values of x and y which satisfy either (1) or (2) will also satisfy the other. Hence the solution of equation (1) is reduced to the solving of such an equation in which it is assumed that $(a, b) = 1$.

Assuming, then, $(a, b) = 1$, by Theorem 2 integers x_0 and y_0 can be found such that $ax_0 + by_0 = 1$. It follows that $x_1 = x_0 c$, $y_1 = y_0 c$ are integers forming a solution of (1) and $ax_1 + by_1 = c$. Now let x, y be any solution of (1) so that $ax + by = c$. By subtraction $a(x - x_1) + b(y - y_1) = 0$ or $a(x - x_1) = - b(y - y_1)$. Then, since $(a, b) = 1$, by Theorem 3, a divides $y - y_1$, and we

---

* The solving of indeterminate equations and systems of equations in integers and rational numbers forms a considerable part of a work on algebra published by Diophantus probably about the middle of the third century A.D.

can write $y - y_1 = at$, where t is an integer. Then $a(x - x_1)$ $= -bat$ or $x - x_1 = -bt$, and

$$(3) \qquad \begin{cases} x = x_1 - bt \\ y = y_1 + at \end{cases}$$

Thus any solution of (1) may be expressed by (3) in terms of a given solution and an integer t. Conversely it is seen by substituting these values of x and y in (1) that they satisfy for arbitrary values of t. Therefore (3) gives all possible solutions of (1) in terms of an initial solution, x_1, y_1.

EXERCISES II

1. Express unity as a linear function of 93 and 41.
2. Express 9 as a linear function of 243 and 171.

Find the general solution, and determine the number of particular solutions having both x and y positive:

3. $65x + 77y = 200$.   **5.** $50x - 63y = 75$.
4. $33x + 19y = 250$.   **6.** $78x - 117y = 97$.
                         7. $51x + 85y = 1037$.

5. Unique factorization theorem. Following Corollary 2 of Theorem 3 we state:

THEOREM 4. *If a product of several integers is divisible by a prime* p, *at least one of the integers is divisible by* p.

For if no one of the integers were divisible by p their product would be prime to p.

From the foregoing properties based ultimately on the Euclidean algorithm, we will now prove the following fundamental theorem, known as the unique factorization theorem, which has been the principal objective of our argument thus far.

THEOREM 5. *Any composite positive integer* N *can be expressed as the product of primes in one and but one way, if we do not distinguish between two arrangements of the same primes.*

For let p_1 be a prime dividing N, and $N = p_1 N_1$. If N_1 is composite it is divisible by a prime p_2, and $N = p_1 \cdot p_2 \cdot N_2$. This process may be continued until N_{k-1} is itself a prime p_k, and

$N = p_1 \cdot p_2 \cdots p_k$, in which the p_i may not be distinct. An abbreviated writing of such a product is $N = \prod\limits_{i=1}^{k} p_i$.

Now suppose a second factorization of N into primes were effected and

$$N = \prod_{i=1}^{k} p_i = \prod_{j=1}^{n} q_j$$

Each p_i divides $\prod\limits_{1}^{n} q_j$, and by Theorem 4 it divides one of the q_j and is therefore identical with it. Let it be that $p_1 = q_1$, then

$$\prod_{2}^{k} p_i = \prod_{2}^{n} q_j$$

By extending the argument each p_i is seen to be identical with some q_j, $k = n$, and the theorem follows.

There is no direct and practicable method of factoring all integers, and at the same time the problem is of fundamental importance in the study of numbers. Several special methods exist by which integers of certain forms may be factored, but all are limited in application. Some of these will receive attention in the progress of our study. An excellent discussion of the problem of finding the factors of an integer is given in the introduction to Lehmer's *Factor Tables*. These tables give the factors of all integers less than 10,000,000.

The primes which divide a number N may be found by the direct method of trial division if N is not too large for the method to be practicable. Such trials may be limited to primes less than or equal to $\sqrt{N}$. For, obviously, if N is the product of two factors, one of them is less than or equal to $\sqrt{N}$. Of course, if N contains either of the primes 2 or 5, that fact is shown at once by the nature of the end digit of N.

For example, we express 6534 in terms of its prime factors. Obviously, 2 is a factor, and $6534 = 2 \cdot 3267$. It is seen that the larger factor contains neither 2 nor 5. By successive trials we find $6534 = 2 \cdot 3^3 \cdot 11^2$.

6. Sum and number of divisors. From the expression of 6534 in terms of its prime factors, all its factors may be listed. They are unity and all possible combinations of one or more of the primes 2, 3, and 11, each with an exponent less than or equal to its exponent in 6534. Clearly these factors are the terms of the product

$$(1+2)(1+3+3^2+3^3)(1+11+11^2)$$

$$= 1+3+3^2+3^3+11+3\cdot11+3^2\cdot11+3^3\cdot11+11^2+3\cdot11^2$$

$$+3^2\cdot11^2+3^3\cdot11^2+2+2\cdot3+2\cdot3^2+2\cdot3^3+2\cdot11+2\cdot3\cdot11$$

$$+2\cdot3^2\cdot11+2\cdot3^3\cdot11+2\cdot11^2+2\cdot3\cdot11^2+2\cdot3^2\cdot11^2$$

$$+2\cdot3^3\cdot11^2$$

This expression, therefore, represents the sum of the divisors of 6534. From the first form in which it is written, it appears that the number of the divisors of 6534 is $2\cdot4\cdot3 = 24$.

These expressions are readily generalized to secure formulas for the sum of the divisors of a number N, and for the number of its divisors, assuming that its prime factors are known. Let $N = p_1^{\alpha_1}\cdot p_2^{\alpha_2}\cdot p_3^{\alpha_3}\cdots p_k^{\alpha_k}$, where the p_i are distinct primes. The divisors of N are unity and all the possible combinations of from 1 to k of the p_i, each having an exponent of any value from 1 to α_i inclusive. These divisors are seen to be the terms obtained by multiplying together the quantities in parentheses in

$$\sigma(N) = (1 + p_1 + p_1^2 + \cdots + p_1^{\alpha_1})(1 + p_2 + p_2^2 + \cdots + p_2^{\alpha_2})$$

$$\cdots(1 + p_k + p_k^2 + \cdots + p_k^{\alpha_k})$$

$$= \frac{p_1^{\alpha_1+1} - 1}{p_1 - 1} \cdot \frac{p_2^{\alpha_2+1} - 1}{p_2 - 1} \cdots \cdot \frac{p_k^{\alpha_k+1} - 1}{p_k - 1}$$

and $\sigma(N)$ is therefore the sum of the divisors. From the first of these forms the number of divisors of N is seen to be

$$\nu(N) = (1 + \alpha_1)(1 + \alpha_2)\cdots\cdot(1 + \alpha_k)$$

To illustrate, put $N = 5,217,520 = 2^4\cdot5\cdot7^2\cdot11^3$.

$$\sigma(N) = (1+2+2^2+2^3+2^4)(1+5)(1+7+7^2)(1+11+11^2+11^3)$$

$$= \frac{2^5 - 1}{2 - 1} \cdot \frac{5^2 - 1}{5 - 1} \cdot \frac{7^3 - 1}{7 - 1} \cdot \frac{11^4 - 1}{11 - 1} = 15,521,328$$

$$\nu(N) = (1 + 4)(1 + 1)(1 + 2)(1 + 3) = 120$$

7. Least common multiple. The least common multiple of two or more integers m_1, m_2, $\cdots$, m_k is the smallest positive integer divisible by each of them. Consider the m_i resolved into their prime factors. Let α_i be the least and β_i the greatest number of times the prime p_i occurs in any one m_j. It follows from the definition that the l.c.m. $= \Pi\, p_i^{\beta_i}$. Also the g.c.d. $= \Pi\, p_i^{\alpha_i}$.

To illustrate, if
$$m_1 = 2 \cdot 3^5 \cdot 7$$
$$m_2 = 2^4 \cdot 3^2 \cdot 11$$
$$m_3 = 2^2 \cdot 3 \cdot 7$$

then the $\qquad$ l.c.m. $= 2^4 \cdot 3^5 \cdot 7 \cdot 11$

and the $\qquad$ g.c.d. $= 2 \cdot 3$

8. Infinitude of primes. *The number of primes is infinite.* Euclid's argument establishing this proposition follows. Assume that there is a largest prime p. Form the product P of all primes $\leq p$ and add 1.

$$P + 1 = 2 \cdot 3 \cdot 5 \cdot 7 \cdots \cdot p + 1 > p$$

If the number $P + 1$ is a prime then p is not the greatest prime. If $P + 1$ is composite it must be the product of primes each of which is greater than p. For, when $P + 1$ is divided by any prime $\leq p$, there is a remainder of $+1$. Thus in any case it is shown that at least one prime exists which is greater than p. Hence there is no greatest prime.

EXERCISES III

1. Find the l.c.m. and the g.c.d. of 4235, 2156, and 2457.

2. Show that the product of the g.c.d. and the l.c.m. of two integers is the product of the integers.

3. Find $\sigma(144)$ and $\nu(144)$ by means of the formulas, and check by listing the divisors.

4. By means of the formulas find the sum of the divisors and the number of the divisors of the integers of Exercise 1.

5. Prove that, if $(m, n) = 1$, then $\sigma(m \cdot n) = \sigma(m)\, \sigma(n)$ and $\nu(m \cdot n) = \nu(m)\, \nu(n)$.

6. Given $m = 2^{p-1}(2^p - 1)$ and $2^p - 1$ is a prime; show that $\sigma(m) = 2m$.

7. Prove that there are infinitely many primes of the form $6n - 1$. *Suggestion:* Use the number $P - 1$, where P is the product of all primes $\leq 6n - 1$.

8. Prove that there are infinitely many primes of the form $4n - 1$.

9. Perfect numbers. A class of numbers which received special attention from the Greeks, and from many students of mathematics since, is made up of those positive integers m such that $\sigma(m) = 2m$. This is equivalent to saying that a number belongs to this class when it equals the sum of all its divisors other than itself. Apparently a little of the mystical regard which the Greeks had for the striking properties of numbers is reflected in their calling this kind of number a *perfect number*. Six is such a number, since $1 + 2 + 3 = 6$, or $\sigma(6) = 12$. The two next smallest perfect numbers are 28 and 496.

In solving Exercise 6 above, the student proved that $m = 2^{n-1}(2^n - 1)$, where $2^n - 1$ is a prime, is always a perfect number. Conversely, we show as follows * that *every even perfect number is of the form* $2^{n-1}(2^n - 1)$, *where* $2^n - 1$ *is a prime*. For let $m = 2^{r-1}q$, where q is odd and $r > 1$, be any even perfect number. Then

$$\sigma(m) = \sigma(2^{r-1}) \cdot \sigma(q) = (2^r - 1) \cdot \sigma(q) = 2m = 2^r q$$

In the equation

$$(2^r - 1) \cdot \sigma(q) = 2^r q$$

we put $\sigma(q) = q + d$, thereby defining d, getting

$$(2^r - 1)(q + d) = 2^r q$$

Solving this for q, we have

$$q = d(2^r - 1)$$

which shows d to be a divisor of q and $< q$. But by assumption $\sigma(q) = q + d$. Hence it is necessary that $d = 1$. For if $d > 1$, then $\sigma(q) \geqq q + d + 1$. Therefore $\sigma(q) = q + 1$, which is true only when q is a prime. Hence

$$q = d(2^r - 1) = 2^r - 1$$

which is a prime.

We thus have some knowledge of the form of all even perfect numbers. This becomes all the more important in the light of the fact that no odd perfect numbers are known. No proof exists, however, that an odd number cannot be perfect.

---

* This proof is due to L. E. Dickson. See *Amer. Math. Monthly*, Vol. 18 (1911), p. 109.

10. Euler ϕ-function. By $\phi(m)$, where m is a positive integer, is meant the number of positive integers not greater than m and prime to it.*

Thus $\phi(1) = 1$, $\phi(2) = 1$, $\phi(3) = 2$, $\phi(4) = 2$. Clearly, if p is a prime, $\phi(p) = p - 1$.

We proceed to derive a formula for $\phi(m)$, where $m = \Pi\, p_i^{\alpha_i}$.

Denote the set of integers 1, 2, 3, $\cdots$, m by M. $\dfrac{m}{p_1}$ of these are multiples of p_1 and hence not prime to m. Then $m - \dfrac{m}{p_1}$ $= m\left(1 - \dfrac{1}{p_1}\right)$ of the integers M are prime to p_1. Denote this set by P_1.

Now P_1 includes those multiples of p_2 which are not also multiples of p_1. We determine their number and thus find the number of integers prime to both p_1 and p_2. All the multiples of p_2 in M are p_2, $2p_2$, $3p_2$, $\cdots$, rp_2, $\cdots$, $\dfrac{m}{p_2}\,p_2$. Those which are in P_1 are the ones in which r is not divisible by p_1. Reasoning as above, $\dfrac{m}{p_2}\left(1 - \dfrac{1}{p_1}\right)$ of the integers 1, 2, 3, $\cdots$, $\dfrac{m}{p_2}$ are not divisible by p_1, which means that $\dfrac{m}{p_2}\left(1 - \dfrac{1}{p_1}\right)$ integers of P_1 are multiples of p_2. Hence, the number of integers of M prime to both p_1 and p_2 is

$$m\left(1 - \frac{1}{p_1}\right) - \frac{m}{p_2}\left(1 - \frac{1}{p_1}\right) = m\left(1 - \frac{1}{p_1}\right)\left(1 - \frac{1}{p_2}\right)$$

We now complete the argument by induction.† Assume that after all integers which are multiples of one or more of the primes p_1, p_2, $\cdots$, p_i are removed from the set M, there are left $m\left(1 - \dfrac{1}{p_1}\right)\left(1 - \dfrac{1}{p_2}\right) \cdots \left(1 - \dfrac{1}{p_i}\right)$ integers denoted by P_i.

---

* Other names for $\phi(m)$ are the totient of m and the indicator of m.

† The reader will recall the basic principle of proof by mathematical induction: If a statement involving an integer n is known to be true for one value of n, say $n = n_0$, and if, assuming it to be true for n in general, we can prove it to be true for $n + 1$, then it follows that the statement is true for $n = n_0 + 1$, $n_0 + 2$, etc., and consequently for all values of $n \geqq n_0$.

All multiples of p_{i+1} in M are

$$p_{i+1},\; 2p_{i+1},\; \cdots,\; rp_{i+1},\; \cdots,\; \frac{m}{p_{i+1}}\, p_{i+1}$$

Those which are in P_i are the ones in which r is not divisible by any of the primes $p_1,\; p_2,\; \cdots,\; p_i$. The number of such is the number of integers in the set $1, 2, 3, \cdots, r, \cdots, \dfrac{m}{p_{i+1}}$ prime to the product $p_1 \cdot p_2 \cdots \cdot p_i$, which number, by the above assumption, is

$$\frac{m}{p_{i+1}}\left(1 - \frac{1}{p_1}\right)\left(1 - \frac{1}{p_2}\right)\cdots\left(1 - \frac{1}{p_i}\right)$$

Subtracting this from the number of integers in the set P_i and factoring the result, we get

$$m\left(1 - \frac{1}{p_1}\right)\left(1 - \frac{1}{p_2}\right)\cdots\left(1 - \frac{1}{p_i}\right)\left(1 - \frac{1}{p_{i+1}}\right)$$

as the number of integers of M which are prime to the product $p_1 \cdot p_2 \cdots \cdot p_{i+1}$. This result is in the same form as that assumed for the number of integers in P_i. Then, since the form was proved to be correct for $i = 1$ and $i = 2$, it holds for all values of i, and therefore:

THEOREM 6. $\displaystyle \phi(m) = m \prod_{i=1}^{k}\left(1 - \frac{1}{p_i}\right) = \prod_{i=1}^{k} p_i^{\alpha_1 - 1}(p_i - 1),$

where $\displaystyle m = \prod_{i=1}^{k} p_i^{\alpha_1}$.

The latter form given for $\phi(m)$ is useful for computation. In particular we note that $\phi(p^\alpha) = p^\alpha\left(1 - \dfrac{1}{p}\right) = p^{\alpha-1}(p - 1)$, where p is a prime.

THEOREM 7.   *When* $(m, n) = 1$, $\phi(m \cdot n) = \phi(m)\phi(n)$.

This follows readily from the last theorem.   If

$$m = \prod_{1}^{k} p_i^{\alpha_i} \quad \text{and} \quad n = \prod_{1}^{l} q_i^{\beta_i},$$

$$\phi(m)\phi(n) = m \prod_{1}^{k}\left(1 - \frac{1}{p_i}\right) n \prod_{1}^{l}\left(1 - \frac{1}{q_i}\right)$$

$$= mn \prod_{1}^{k}\left(1 - \frac{1}{p_i}\right) \prod_{1}^{l}\left(1 - \frac{1}{q_i}\right) = \phi(mn)$$

EXERCISES IV

1. Find the values of $\phi(144)$ and $\phi(360)$.

2. Find the value of $\phi(6615)$.

3. Show that $\displaystyle\sum_{i=0}^{\alpha} \phi(p^i) = p^\alpha$, where p is a prime.

4. Show that the sum of the totients of the divisors of any integer equals the integer.

5. Show that, if $n > 1$, the sum of the positive integers less than n and prime to n is $\dfrac{n}{2}\phi(n)$.

11. The equation $\phi(x) = n$. Given n, there is no known formula by which x can be determined so as to satisfy $\phi(x) = n$. But the following process enables us to compute x in any given case, and is quite practicable if n is sufficiently small.

Let $x = \Pi\, p_i^{\alpha_i}$; then $\phi(x) = \Pi\, p_i^{\alpha_i}\dfrac{p_i - 1}{p_i} = n$. Put $p_i - 1 = d_i$; then d_i is a divisor of n and $n = \Pi\, p_i^{\alpha_i}\dfrac{d_i}{p_i} = x\,\Pi\,\dfrac{d_i}{p_i}$. Therefore

$$x = \frac{n}{\Pi\, d_i}\cdot \Pi\, p_i$$

Here $\Pi\, d_i$ may be the product of any of the divisors d_i of n such that each $d_i + 1$ is a prime p_i; and subject to the further condition that $\dfrac{n}{\Pi\, p_i}$ is an integer containing no prime factor not included in $\Pi\, p_i$, for $\Pi\, p_i$ is by definition the product of all the distinct prime factors of x.

Illustrative example. Find the values of x for which $\phi(x) = 12$. The values of d_i such that $d_i + 1 = p_i$ are 1, 2, 4, 6, 12. In considering all possible $\Pi\, d_i$ we may at once eliminate those in which $\dfrac{n}{\Pi\, d_i}$ is not an integer, such, for example, as $2\cdot 4$ and $4\cdot 6$, since $\dfrac{12}{2\cdot 4}$ and $\dfrac{12}{4\cdot 6}$ are not integers.

Also the further condition that $\dfrac{n}{\Pi\, d_i}$ shall have no prime factor not also a factor of $\Pi\,(d_i + 1) = \Pi\, p_i$ causes the elimination of such $\Pi\, d_i$ as, for instance, 2 or $1\cdot 4$. For, when $\Pi\, d_i = 2$, $\dfrac{n}{\Pi\, d_i} = \dfrac{12}{2} = 2\cdot 3$, and $\Pi\, p_i = 3$, which does not have 2 as a divisor; and when

$\Pi\, d_i = 1\cdot4,\ \dfrac{n}{\Pi\, d_i} = \dfrac{12}{1\cdot4} = 3$, while $\Pi\, p_i = 2\cdot5$, of which 3 is not a divisor.

The values of $\Pi\, d_i$ which satisfy all conditions and the resulting solutions are:

$\Pi\, d_i$:	12	$1\cdot2$	$1\cdot6$	$1\cdot12$	$2\cdot6$	$1\cdot2\cdot6$
$\dfrac{n}{\Pi\, d_i}$:	1	6	2	1	1	1
$\Pi\, p_i$:	13	$2\cdot3$	$2\cdot7$	$2\cdot13$	$3\cdot7$	$2\cdot3\cdot7$
x :	13	36	28	26	21	42

EXERCISES V

1. Find the values of x for which $\phi(x) = 24$.

2. Find the values of x for which $\phi(x) = 72$.

3. Show that $\phi(x) = 2p$, where p is a prime and $2p + 1$ is composite, has no solution.

4. Find a set of ten consecutive integers all of which are composite.

5. Find all possible numbers $m = 2^n\cdot3\cdot p$ (p an odd prime) such that $3m = \sigma(m)$.

6. Find the smallest number having sixteen divisors.

7. If $(a, b) = 1$, show that $a + b$ and $a^2 - ab + b^2$ can have no common factor unless $a + b$ is a multiple of 3.

8. If $(a, b) = 1$, and p is an odd prime, show that $\dfrac{a^p + b^p}{a + b}$ and $a + b$ have no common factor unless $a + b$ is a multiple of p.

9. If $f(x)$ is a polynomial, it cannot represent only primes for integral values of x. *Suggestion:* Let $u = f(m)$ and $v = f(m + ku)$, where k is any integer. Prove that u is a factor of v.

10. Show that $10^n + 3\cdot4^{n+2} + 5$ is divisible by 9. *Suggestion:* Denote the function by $f(n)$, and show that $f(n + 1) - f(n)$ is divisible by 9. Then use induction.

11. Show that $7^{2n} + 16n - 1$ is divisible by 64.

12. Show that, if p is a prime, $x^p - x$ is divisible by p.

CHAPTER II

SIMPLE CONTINUED FRACTIONS

12. Expansion of rational numbers. An expression of the form

$$a_1 + \cfrac{b_1}{a_2 + \cfrac{b_2}{a_3 + \cfrac{b_3}{a_4 + \cdots}}}$$

is called a *continued fraction*. In general, the a_i and b_i may be unrestricted in character, and the number of terms may be finite or infinite.

A *simple* continued fraction, s.c.f., is one in which each $b_i = 1$ and the a_i are positive integers, except that a_1 may be positive, negative, or zero. Our discussion will be limited to simple continued fractions.

A more convenient writing of them is $a_1 + \cfrac{1}{a_2} + \cfrac{1}{a_3} + \cfrac{1}{a_4} + \cdots$ or, yet more simply, $(a_1, a_2, a_3, a_4 \cdots)$.

The properties of simple continued fractions will have several interesting applications in our study of the integers.

The following illustrates the expansion of rational numbers into simple continued fractions:

$$\frac{67}{24} = 2 + \frac{19}{24} = 2 + \cfrac{1}{\cfrac{24}{19}} = 2 + \cfrac{1}{1 + \cfrac{5}{19}} = 2 + \cfrac{1}{1} + \cfrac{1}{3} + \cfrac{1}{1} + \cfrac{1}{4}$$

Or, in the case of a negative number,

$$-\frac{67}{24} = -3 + \frac{5}{24} = -3 + \cfrac{1}{4 + \cfrac{4}{5}} = -3 + \cfrac{1}{4} + \cfrac{1}{1} + \cfrac{1}{4}$$

These illustrations generalize readily to yield the proof of:

THEOREM 1. *Any rational number may be expanded into a simple continued fraction with a finite number of terms, and the expansion is unique.*

Let $\frac{p}{q}$ be any rational number. Then by division $\frac{p}{q} = a_1 + \frac{r_1}{q}$, where a_1 is the greatest integer $\leqq \frac{p}{q}$ *and* $0 \leqq r_1 < q$. If $\frac{p}{q}$ is negative, a_1 will be negative and is so chosen that r_1 will not be negative. Likewise $\frac{q}{r_1} = a_2 + \frac{r_2}{r_1}, \frac{r_1}{r_2} = a_3 + \frac{r_3}{r_2}, \cdots$, in which each a_i is the greatest integer in the corresponding fraction and $r_{i+1} < r_i$. Since the r_i are non-negative integers that decrease with each step, after a finite number n of steps r_n must be zero and the process ends. (For there are only a finite number of non-negative integers less than a given integer.) Combining the results of the n steps,

$$\frac{p}{q} = a_1 + \frac{1}{a_2 +} \frac{1}{a_3 +} \cdots + \frac{1}{a_n} \cdot a_i \text{ is called the } i\text{th partial quotient,}$$

and $a_i + \frac{r_i}{r_{i-1}}$ the ith complete quotient.

That this expansion is unique follows from the manner in which each a_i is chosen. This should be accompanied, however, by the remark that the number of terms in a finite simple continued fraction can always be changed by 1. For if $a_n > 1$ it can be replaced by $(a_n - 1) + \frac{1}{1}$. That is, if $a_n = 3$, it can be replaced by $2 + \frac{1}{1}$. And if $a_n = 1$ we have $a_{n-1} + \frac{1}{1}$ which can be replaced by $a_{n-1} + 1$, as $3 + \frac{1}{1}$ can be replaced by 4. Hence, in the expansion of a rational number, the number of partial quotients may be assumed to be either even or odd, unless the choice is restricted by some other imposed condition. Such a condition is met later in the exercises on symmetric continued fractions.

The algorithm for expanding $\frac{p}{q}$ into a simple continued fraction is identical with the Euclidean algorithm for finding the g.c.d. of

p and q.   This algorithm gives the equations

$$p = a_1 q + r_1$$

$$q = a_2 r_1 + r_2$$

. . . . . .

. . . . . .

which may be written

$$\frac{p}{q} = a_1 + \frac{r_1}{q}$$

$$\frac{q}{r_1} = a_2 + \frac{r_2}{r_1}$$

. . . . .

. . . . .

and when these are combined the continued fraction is secured.

13. Convergents.   That part of the simple continued fraction up to and including a_k is called the kth *convergent*, and is denoted by C_k.   In the expansion of $\dfrac{67}{24}$, $C_3 = 2 + \dfrac{1}{1} + \dfrac{1}{3} = \dfrac{11}{4}$.

In general, $C_1 = a_1 = \dfrac{a_1}{1}$.   We shall put $p_1 = a_1$ and $q_1 = 1$, so   that $C_1 = \dfrac{p_1}{q_1}$. $C_2 = a_1 + \dfrac{1}{a_2} = \dfrac{a_2 a_1 + 1}{a_2}$,   and   we   put $p_2 = a_2 a_1 + 1$, $q_2 = a_2$.   Then $C_2 = \dfrac{p_2}{q_2}$. $C_3 = a_1 + \dfrac{1}{a_2 + \dfrac{1}{a_3}}$ $= \dfrac{a_3(a_2 a_1 + 1) + a_1}{a_3 a_2 + 1} = \dfrac{p_3}{q_3}$ if we put $p_3 = a_3(a_2 a_1 + 1) + a_1 = a_3 p_2 + p_1$, and $q_3 = a_3 a_2 + 1 = a_3 q_2 + q_1$.

The algorithm here suggested for computing any p_i and q_i from the   preceding   values   in   such   a   way   that $C_i = \dfrac{p_i}{q_i}$ may   be established by induction.

For   all $i \geqq 3$, we   define $p_i = a_i p_{i-1} + p_{i-2}$ and $q_i = a_i q_{i-1} + q_{i-2}$, and assume $C_i = \dfrac{p_i}{q_i} = \dfrac{a_i p_{i-1} + p_{i-2}}{a_i q_{i-1} + q_{i-2}}$.   Then C_{i+1} may, from its very definition, be had by putting $a_i + \dfrac{1}{a_{i+1}}$ for a_i in the expression for C_i, getting

$$C_{i+1} = \frac{\left(a_i + \dfrac{1}{a_{i+1}}\right) p_{i-1} + p_{i-2}}{\left(a_i + \dfrac{1}{a_{i+1}}\right) q_{i-1} + q_{i-2}} = \frac{a_{i+1}(a_i p_{i-1} + p_{i-2}) + p_{i-1}}{a_{i+1}(a_i q_{i-1} + q_{i-2}) + q_{i-1}}$$

$$= \frac{a_{i+1} p_i + p_{i-1}}{a_{i+1} q_i + q_{i-1}} = \frac{p_{i+1}}{q_{i+1}}$$

which is the result to be proved with i replaced by $i + 1$. This proves the algorithm $p_i = a_i p_{i-1} + p_{i-2}$, $q_i = a_i q_{i-1} + q_{i-2}$, $C_i = \dfrac{p_i}{q_i}$ to be valid for the computation of all C_i for $i \geqq 3$, since we have seen that it is valid for $i = 3$. To extend it to include $i = 1$ and $i = 2$ we define $p_{-1} = 0$, $p_0 = 1$, $q_{-1} = 1$, and $q_0 = 0$; for these values enable us to write

$$p_1 = a_1 p_0 + p_{-1} \qquad q_1 = a_1 q_0 + q_{-1}$$

$$p_2 = a_2 p_1 + p_0 \qquad q_2 = a_2 q_1 + q_0$$

thus making the algorithm valid for all values of i. We shall not call $\dfrac{p_{-1}}{q_{-1}}$ and $\dfrac{p_0}{q_0}$ convergents.

It is important to note that this method of computing the convergents of a simple continued fraction by means of *recurrence relations* is independent of whether the fraction has a finite or an infinite number of terms.

A convenient arrangement of the computation of the convergents is shown in the following. Given the continued fraction $(2, 1, 3, 1, 4, 2, \cdots)$; arrange the a_i, p_{-1}, p_0, q_{-1}, and q_0 as shown, and the computation proceeds by the above formulas.

i	-1	0	1	2	3	4	5	6	$\cdots$
a_i			2	1	3	1	4	2	$\cdots$
p_i	0	1	2	3	11	14	67	148	$\cdots$
q_i	1	0	1	1	4	5	24	53	$\cdots$

For example, this shows that $C_5 = \dfrac{p_5}{q_5} = \dfrac{67}{24} = (2, 1, 3, 1, 4)$.

Since $\dfrac{p_n}{q_n}$ is a rational function of the preceding p_i, q_i, and a_n, and therefore a rational function of the a_i, all of which are integers, we can state:

THEOREM 2. *Any simple continued fraction with a finite number of terms represents a rational number.*

EXERCISES I

Expand into simple continued fractions:

1. $\frac{119}{32}$.
2. $\frac{426}{359}$.
3. $\frac{118}{303}$.
4. $-\frac{46}{39}$.

Find the numbers represented by:

5. $(3, 1, 1, 4, 1, 3)$.
6. $(0, 2, 4, 1, 5)$.
7. $(2, 1, 1, 3, 1, 1, 2)$.
8. $(-5, 1, 3, 2, 4)$.

9. Prove that $\dfrac{p_n}{p_{n-1}} = (a_n, a_{n-1}, \cdots, a_2, a_1)$.

10. Prove that $\dfrac{q_n}{q_{n-1}} = (a_n, a_{n-1}, \cdots, a_3, a_2)$.

11. Compute the successive convergents to 3.14159.

12 Show that the kth convergent in the expansion of $\dfrac{1}{x}$ is the reciprocal of the $(k-1)$th convergent in the expansion of x.

14. Differences of convergents.
Attentive inspection of some of the preceding exercises leads to two observations: first, that the convergents always seem to be in lowest terms; and second, that the difference of two consecutive convergents is a fraction with numerator unity. We proceed to prove these results.

THEOREM 3. $p_n q_{n-1} - p_{n-1} q_n = (-1)^n$, *where* $n \geqq 0$.

To prove this we use the values of p_n and q_n obtained above and write

$$p_n q_{n-1} - p_{n-1} q_n = (a_n p_{n-1} + p_{n-2})q_{n-1} - p_{n-1}(a_n q_{n-1} + q_{n-2})$$

$$= -(p_{n-1} q_{n-2} - p_{n-2} q_{n-1})$$

This expression in the parentheses is the same as the original with $n - 1$ put for n. Then by repeating this reduction until it has been performed n times we get

$$p_n q_{n-1} - p_{n-1} q_n = (-1)^n (p_0 q_{-1} - p_{-1} q_0) = (-1)^n$$

and the theorem is proved.

COROLLARY 1.   *Each convergent $\dfrac{p_n}{q_n}$ of a simple continued frac-*
tion is in its lowest terms.

This follows by observing that p_n and q_n can have no common factor which is not a divisor of $(-1)^n$.

However, the fraction obtained by expanding a number $\dfrac{p}{q}$ is the same whether or not $\dfrac{p}{q}$ is first reduced to its lowest terms.

COROLLARY 2. $\dfrac{p_n}{q_n} - \dfrac{p_{n-1}}{q_{n-1}} = \dfrac{(-1)^n}{q_n q_{n-1}}$, *where* $n \geqq 2$.

This is obtained by dividing through the equation of the theorem by $q_n q_{n-1}$.

This result is significant in that it puts in very useful form the value of the difference between two successive convergents.

There is also a useful formula for the difference of two convergents whose indices differ by 2.

THEOREM 4. $\dfrac{p_n}{q_n} - \dfrac{p_{n-2}}{q_{n-2}} = \dfrac{(-1)^{n-1} a_n}{q_n q_{n-2}}$ $n \geqq 3.$*

For by substituting for p_n and q_n

$$p_n q_{n-2} - p_{n-2} q_n = (a_n p_{n-1} + p_{n-2}) q_{n-2} - p_{n-2}(a_n q_{n-1} + q_{n-2})$$

$$= a_n(p_{n-1} q_{n-2} - p_{n-2} q_{n-1}) = a_n(-1)^{n-1}$$

Then, by dividing through the equation

$$p_n q_{n-2} - p_{n-2} q_n = a_n(-1)^{n-1} \text{ by } q_n q_{n-2}$$

we get $\dfrac{p_n}{q_n} - \dfrac{p_{n-2}}{q_{n-2}} = \dfrac{(-1)^{n-1} a_n}{q_n q_{n-2}}$

15. Another solution of $ax + by = c$.   This equation was discussed and solved in Chapter I by means of the algorithm used in finding the g.c.d. of two integers.   It may be solved also by use of the equation of Theorem 3.   Assume $(a, b) = 1$, and expand $\dfrac{a}{b}$ into a simple continued fraction.   Then with $a = p_n$ and $b = q_n$

$$a q_{n-1} - b p_{n-1} = (-1)^n$$

* The equation holds also for $n = 1$.

and multiplying through by $(-1)^n C$,

$$a[(-1)^n C q_{n-1}] + b[(-1)^{n+1} C p_{n-1}] = C$$

Thus one solution of the equation is

$$x_1 = (-1)^n C q_{n-1}$$
$$y_1 = (-1)^{n+1} C p_{n-1}$$

and, as before, the general solution may be written

$$x = x_1 - bt$$
$$y = y_1 + at$$

in which t is any integer—positive, negative, or zero.

EXERCISES II

1. Using a continued fraction, find the general solution in integers of $101x + 68y = 50$. Discuss the number of solutions in which both x and y are positive.

2. The same for $75x - 131y = 62$.

A symmetric continued fraction is a finite simple continued fraction in which the partial quotients read the same both ways. *Examples:* $\frac{247}{77} = (3, 4, 1, 4, 3)$, $\frac{425}{132} = (3, 4, 1, 1, 4, 3)$.

3. Prove that if a rational number $\frac{p}{q} > 1$, $(p, q) = 1$, expands into a symmetric continued fraction, then $q^2 + 1$ or $q^2 - 1$ is divisible by p according as the number of partial quotients is even or odd. *Suggestion:* Use Exercise I, 9.

4. Conversely, prove that according as $q_n^2 + 1$ or $q_n^2 - 1$ is divisible by p_n, where $p_n > q_n > 0$, $\frac{p_n}{q_n}$ develops into a symmetric continued fraction with an even or an odd number of partial quotients. *Suggestion:* Put $q_n^2 + (-1)^n = p_n r$, and recall that $p_{n-1} q_n + (-1)^n = p_n q_{n-1}$. By subtraction $(q_n - p_{n-1}) q_n = p_n (r - q_{n-1})$. Note that q_n divides the right member and p_n divides the left member.

5. Write the fraction $(3, 1, 1, 2, 2, 1, 1, 2, 1)$ in symmetric form, and verify the proposition in Exercise 3.

6. Verify the proposition in Exercise 4 for three of the divisors of $13^2 + 1 = 170$.

7. Verify the proposition in Exercise 4 for six of the divisors of $13^2 - 1 = 168$.

16. Expansion of irrational numbers. THEOREM 5. *The odd convergents of a simple continued fraction form an increasing sequence and the even convergents form a decreasing sequence, and every odd convergent is less than any even convergent.*

From Corollary 2 of Theorem 3,

$$(1) \qquad C_n - C_{n-1} = \frac{(-1)^n}{q_n q_{n-1}} \text{ for } n \geqq 2$$

and from Theorem 4

$$C_n - C_{n-2} = \frac{(-1)^{n-1} a_n}{q_n q_{n-2}} \text{ for } n \geqq 3$$

From a comparison of these expressions it appears that $C_n - C_{n-1}$ and $C_n - C_{n-2}$ have opposite signs and hence C_n lies between C_{n-1} and C_{n-2}. That is, each convergent of a simple continued fraction lies between the two preceding convergents.

From (1), $C_1 < C_2$. Then it follows that $C_1 < C_3 < C_2$, $C_3 < C_4 < C_2$, $C_3 < C_5 < C_4$, $C_5 < C_6 < C_4$, $\cdots$, etc. These inequalities may be combined; thus $C_1 < C_3 < C_5 < \cdots \quad \cdots < C_6 < C_4 < C_2$. If we notice that when each C_i is written in this sequence it must be placed between C_{i-1} and C_{i-2}, the truth of the theorem appears.

Theorem 5 applies whether the number of terms in the simple continued fraction is finite or infinite. We have already seen that a rational number can be expanded into a terminating simple continued fraction, and, conversely, a terminating simple continued fraction represents a rational number, namely, its last convergent. Theorem 5 will prove immediately useful in studying the relation between infinite continued fractions and irrational numbers.

THEOREM 6. *Every infinite simple continued fraction converges to a limit which is greater than any odd convergent and less than any even convergent.*

For, since the C_{2k-1} form an increasing sequence which is limited to being less than any C_{2k}, they converge to a limit as k tends to infinity. Similarly the decreasing sequence formed by the C_{2k} is convergent.

Now, since $q_n = a_n q_{n-1} + q_{n-2}$, the q_i increase without limit as i tends to infinity. Then

$$\lim_{k \to \infty} |C_{2k} - C_{2k-1}| = \lim_{k \to \infty} \frac{1}{q_{2k} q_{2k-1}} = 0$$

Hence both sequences converge to the same limit l, and for all positive values of k

$$C_{2k-1} < l < C_{2k}$$

THEOREM 7. *Any irrational number* x *can be expanded into an infinite simple continued fraction.*

Let a_1 be the greatest integer $< x$.

Then $x = a_1 + \dfrac{1}{x_2}$, where $0 < \dfrac{1}{x_2} < 1$ and $x_2 > 1$ and irrational.

Again, $x_2 = a_2 + \dfrac{1}{x_3}$, where $a_2 \geq 1$ is the greatest integer in x_2 and $x_3 > 1$. This process may be continued indefinitely with $x_n = a_n + \dfrac{1}{x_{n+1}}$, in which $a_n \geq 1$ is the greatest integer in x_n and $x_{n+1} > 1$. For the process cannot terminate because, if at any stage $x_i = a_i$, x would be rational. Thus we arrive at the infinite simple continued fraction

$$a_1 + \frac{1}{a_2 +} \frac{1}{a_3 +} \cdots + \frac{1}{a_n +} \cdots$$

Illustrative example. Expand $\sqrt{7}$.

$$\sqrt{7} = 2 + (\sqrt{7} - 2) = 2 + \cfrac{1}{\cfrac{1}{\sqrt{7} - 2}} = 2 + \cfrac{1}{\cfrac{\sqrt{7} + 2}{3}}$$

$$= 2 + \cfrac{1}{1 + \cfrac{\sqrt{7} - 1}{3}} = 2 + \cfrac{1}{1 + \cfrac{1}{\cfrac{\sqrt{7} + 1}{2}}}$$

$$= 2 + \cfrac{1}{1 + \cfrac{1}{1 + \cfrac{\sqrt{7} - 1}{2}}} = 2 + \frac{1}{1 +} \frac{1}{1 +} \cfrac{1}{1 + \cfrac{\sqrt{7} - 2}{3}}$$

$$= 2 + \frac{1}{1 +} \frac{1}{1 +} \frac{1}{1 +} \frac{1}{4 + (\sqrt{7} - 2)}$$

Notice that, following the partial quotient 4, $\dfrac{1}{x_6} = \sqrt{7} - 2$,

which is identical with $\dfrac{1}{x_2}$. Hence $a_2 = a_6 = a_{10} = \cdots$,
$a_3 = a_7 = a_{11} = \cdots$, etc., and $\sqrt{7} = (2, 1, 1, 1, 4, 1, 1, 1, 4, \cdots)$.

Later we shall find such periodicity to be a characteristic of the expansions of all quadratic surds.

THEOREM 8. *Let* x *be expanded into* $(a_1, a_2, \cdots, a_n, \cdots)$ *in accordance with Theorem 7. Then the limit to which the fraction* $(a_1, a_2, \cdots a_n, \cdots)$ *converges in accordance with Theorem 6 is the number* x.

We have
$$x = a_1 + \frac{1}{a_2 +} \cdots + \frac{1}{x_n}$$

$$C_n = a_1 + \frac{1}{a_2 +} \cdots + \frac{1}{a_n}$$

$$C_{n+1} = a_1 + \frac{1}{a_2 +} \cdots + \frac{1}{a_n +} \frac{1}{a_{n+1}}$$

Now
$$x_n = a_n + \frac{1}{x_{n+1}}, \text{ with } x_{n+1} > a_{n+1}$$

Then
$$a_n < x_n < a_n + \frac{1}{a_{n+1}}$$

From this it follows that of C_n and C_{n+1} one will be less and the other greater than x. That is x lies between any two consecutive convergents. Then from Theorem 5 it follows that one set of alternate convergents will all be less than, and the other set all greater than, x. Hence, since $C_1 < x < C_2$, we can write

$$C_{2k-1} < x < C_{2k}$$

Then, since C_{2k-1} and C_{2k} tend to the same limit as k tends to infinity, this limit must be x. Therefore we may now write

$$x = a_1 + \frac{1}{a_2 +} \frac{1}{a_3 +} \cdots + \frac{1}{a_n +} \cdots$$

It remains for us to prove:

THEOREM 9. *The expansion of any irrational number into an infinite simple continued fraction is unique.*

Suppose that
$$x = a_1 + \frac{1}{a_2 +} \frac{1}{a_3 +} \cdots$$

and also
$$x = b_1 + \frac{1}{b_2 +} \frac{1}{b_3 +} \cdots$$

Then $a_1 = b_1$, since each is the greatest integer less than x, and

$$a_2 + \cfrac{1}{a_3 + \cdots} = b_2 + \cfrac{1}{b_3 + \cdots}$$

similarly $a_2 = b_2$, and in the same way $a_3 = b_3$, $\cdots$, $a_n = b_n$, for all values of n, and the fractions are identical.

We can now speak definitely of the value of an infinite simple continued fraction and know the number thus indicated is the number whose expansion gives the fraction. Then, since a rational number expands uniquely into a finite simple continued fraction, we state:

THEOREM 10. *The value of any infinite simple continued fraction is an irrational number.*

17. Approximation theorems. The convergents of the simple continued fraction for an irrational number x constitute an especially important sequence of rational numbers having x as limit. For we shall see presently that in a certain sense these convergents are the " best possible " rational approximations to x. To this end we study a little more carefully how they approach their limit.

THEOREM 11. *Each convergent is nearer the value of a simple continued fraction than is the preceding convergent.*

By putting the complete quotient x_{n+1} for a_{n+1} in

$$C_{n+1} = \frac{a_{n+1}p_n + p_{n-1}}{a_{n+1}q_n + q_{n-1}}$$

we may write

$$x = \frac{x_{n+1}p_n + p_{n-1}}{x_{n+1}q_n + q_{n-1}}$$

From this we get

$$x_{n+1}(xq_n - p_n) = - (xq_{n-1} - p_{n-1}) = - q_{n-1}\left(x - \frac{p_{n-1}}{q_{n-1}}\right)$$

Dividing through by $x_{n+1}q_n$,

$$x - \frac{p_n}{q_n} = - \frac{q_{n-1}}{x_{n+1}q_n}\left(x - \frac{p_{n-1}}{q_{n-1}}\right)$$

Therefore, since $x_{n+1} > 1$ and $q_n > q_{n-1}$,

$$\left| x - \frac{p_n}{q_n} \right| < \left| x - \frac{p_{n-1}}{q_{n-1}} \right|$$

which is the theorem.

Upper and lower limits for the error involved in taking C_n for x are easily inferred from some of the above theorems. By Corollary 2 of Theorem 3,

$$|C_{n+1} - C_n| = \frac{1}{q_n q_{n+1}}$$

Now x lies between C_{n+1} and C_n, and, by Theorem 11, is nearer to C_{n+1}. Therefore

$$\frac{1}{2q_n q_{n+1}} < |x - C_n| < \frac{1}{q_n q_{n+1}}$$

This is sometimes known as the *approximation theorem*.

Illustrative example. Find a ratio involving smaller numbers which can be used instead of $\dfrac{2785}{1232}$ with accuracy to three decimal places.

$$\frac{2785}{1232} = (2, 3, 1, 5, 5, 1, 3, 2). \quad C_4 = \frac{52}{23}, \quad C_5 = \frac{269}{119}$$

It is found that the error ϵ involved in using $\dfrac{52}{23}$ satisfies the inequalities

$$\frac{1}{2 \cdot 23 \cdot 119} < \epsilon < \frac{1}{23 \cdot 119} \quad \text{or} \quad 0.00018 < \epsilon < 0.00037$$

THEOREM 12. *If* $\left| \dfrac{r}{s} - x \right| < |C_n - x|$, r *and* s *being integers,* s > 0, n > 1, *then* s > q_n.

That is, a rational fraction nearer to a given number than one of the convergents in the simple continued fraction for that number must have a larger denominator than the convergent.

This makes precise the sense in which the convergents are the best possible rational approximations to a given number.

Since x lies between C_n and C_{n-1} and is nearer C_n, and by hypothesis $\dfrac{r}{s}$ is nearer x than C_n is, then $\dfrac{r}{s}$ also lies between C_n and C_{n-1}. Hence

$$\left| \frac{p_n}{q_n} - \frac{p_{n-1}}{q_{n-1}} \right| > \left| \frac{r}{s} - \frac{p_{n-1}}{q_{n-1}} \right|$$

and

$$\frac{1}{q_n q_{n-1}} > \frac{|r q_{n-1} - s p_{n-1}|}{s q_{n-1}}$$

Multiplying the inequality by $q_n q_{n-1} s$, we get

$$s > q_n |r q_{n-1} - s p_{n-1}|$$

Now $z = |r q_{n-1} - s p_{n-1}|$ is an integer. z cannot be zero, for then $\frac{r}{s} = \frac{p_{n-1}}{q_{n-1}}$, and the hypothesis would contradict Theorem 11. Therefore $z \geqq 1$ and $s > q_n$.

THEOREM 13. *If* $\left| \dfrac{p_n}{q_n} - x \right| < \dfrac{1}{2 q_n^2}$, *then* $\dfrac{p_n}{q_n}$ *is one of the convergents in the expansion of* x *into a simple continued fraction.*

Expanding $\dfrac{p_n}{q_n}$ into a s.c.f. we have

$$\frac{p_n}{q_n} = (a_1, a_2, \cdots, a_n).$$

From this $\dfrac{1}{2 q_n^2} < \dfrac{1}{q_n(q_n + q_{n-1})}$ and we replace the inequality of the theorem by

$$\left| \frac{p_n}{q_n} - x \right| < \frac{1}{q_n(q_n + q_{n-1})}$$

Letting x_{n+1} be defined by

$$x = a_1 + \frac{1}{a_2} + \cdots + \frac{1}{a_n} + \frac{1}{x_{n+1}}$$

we have

$$x = \frac{x_{n+1} p_n + p_{n-1}}{x_{n+1} q_n + q_{n-1}}$$

from which

(1)
$$x_{n+1} = \frac{x q_{n-1} - p_{n-1}}{p_n - x q_n}$$

We first assume n even, which means that $\dfrac{p_n}{q_n} - x > 0$. Put $\dfrac{p_n}{q_n} - x = \epsilon$ and by it eliminate x from (1) getting

$$x_{n+1} = \frac{1 - \epsilon q_n q_{n-1}}{\epsilon q_n^2}$$

Now the necessary and sufficient condition that $x_{n+1} > 1$ is that $1 - \epsilon q_n q_{n-1} > \epsilon q_n^2$, or $\epsilon < \dfrac{1}{q_n(q_n + q_{n-1})}$. But as seen above this is implied in the hypothesis. Hence $x_{n+1} > 1$. This result is obtained also for n odd, i.e., with $\dfrac{p_n}{q_n} - x < 0$, by putting $x - \dfrac{p_n}{q_n} = \epsilon$ and proceeding as before.

Now expand x into a s.c.f. getting $x = b_1 + \dfrac{1}{b_2} + \cdots + \dfrac{1}{b_n} + \dfrac{1}{y_{n+1}}$ where $y_{n+1} > 1$. Then

$$a_1 + \frac{1}{a_2} + \cdots + \frac{1}{a_n} + \frac{1}{x_{n+1}} = b_1 + \frac{1}{b_2} + \cdots + \frac{1}{b_n} + \frac{1}{y_{n+1}}$$

from which it follows that

$$a_1 = b_1, \ a_2 = b_2, \ \cdots, \ a_n = b_n, \ x_{n+1} = y_{n+1}$$

Hence $\dfrac{p_n}{q_n}$ is the nth convergent in the s.c.f. expansion of x.

EXERCISES III

1. Find limits for the error involved in using $\frac{22}{7}$ for π.

2. Expand $\sqrt{19}$ to four terms of a simple continued fraction, and find C_4.

3. Find the limits of error involved in taking C_4 for $\sqrt{32} = (5, 1, 1, 1, 10, 1, \cdots)$.

18. Recurring simple continued fractions. We have found that rational numbers may be expressed as terminating simple continued fractions and irrational numbers as non-terminating fractions. The special type of non-terminating continued fraction which is periodic was illustrated above in the expansion of $\sqrt{7}$. It will be shown that all infinite periodic fractions represent quadratic surds. First we illustrate by finding the number

$$x = (3, 1, 2, 4, 1, 2, 4, \cdots)$$

which is more conveniently written

$$x = (3, \overline{1, 2, 4})$$

the line above indicating the recurring *period*.   Let $y = (\overline{1, 2, 4})$.
Then

$$y = 1 + \cfrac{1}{2 +} \cfrac{1}{4 +} \cfrac{1}{y}$$

In this terminating fraction, $y = C_4 = \dfrac{13y + 3}{9y + 2}$.   Then

$$9y^2 - 11y - 3 = 0$$

and $y = \dfrac{11 \pm \sqrt{229}}{18}$ · But $y > 0$;   therefore $y = \dfrac{11 + \sqrt{229}}{18}$ ·
Then

$$x = 3 + \frac{1}{y} = \frac{3y + 1}{y} = \frac{7 + \sqrt{229}}{6}$$

This process is readily generalized to prove:

THEOREM 14.   *Every periodic simple continued fraction represents a quadratic surd.*

To prove this let

$$x = (a_1, a_2, \cdots, a_r, \overline{\alpha_1, \alpha_2, \cdots, \alpha_s})$$

represent any such fraction, and let

$$y = (\overline{\alpha_1, \alpha_2, \cdots, \alpha_s}) = \alpha_1 + \cfrac{1}{\alpha_2 +} \cdots + \cfrac{1}{\alpha_s +} \cfrac{1}{y} \qquad (\alpha_1 > 0)$$

from which

$$y = \frac{p_s y + p_{s-1}}{q_s y + q_{s-1}} \qquad (p_{s-1}, \quad p_s, \quad q_{s-1}, \quad q_s \text{ are all} > 0)$$

and $$q_s y^2 + (q_{s-1} - p_s)y - p_{s-1} = 0$$

This quadratic equation has one positive and one negative root,
since its first and last terms have opposite signs.   The positive
root is in fact

$$y = \frac{p_s - q_{s-1} + \sqrt{(q_{s-1} - p_s)^2 + 4p_{s-1}q_s}}{2q_s}$$

which is irrational, since y is the value of a non-terminating
fraction.   Now

$$x = a_1 + \cfrac{1}{a_2 +} \cdots + \cfrac{1}{a_r +} \cfrac{1}{y}$$

Then
$$x = \frac{p'_r y + p'_{r-1}}{q'_r y + q'_{r-1}}$$

which is a rational function of y, and therefore will reduce to a quadratic surd $A + B\sqrt{C}$, where A and B are rational, and C is a positive integer not a square.

19. Expansion of quadratic surds. Let $\dfrac{\sqrt{D} + P}{Q}$ be *any* quadratic surd, D, P, and Q being integers, $D > 0$ and not a square, and $Q \neq 0$. The sign before the radical is assumed positive. Sometimes P and Q will be written P_1 and Q_1 in order to conform to general notation.

We now generalize the method used in the expansion of $\sqrt{7}$ in illustrating Theorem 7. Let a_1 be the greatest integer $< \dfrac{\sqrt{D} + P}{Q}$. It may be negative or zero. Then

$$\frac{\sqrt{D} + P_1}{Q_1} = a_1 + \left(\frac{\sqrt{D} + P_1}{Q_1} - a_1 \right) = a_1 + \frac{\sqrt{D} + P_1 - a_1 Q_1}{Q_1}$$

$$= a_1 + \frac{1}{\dfrac{Q_1[\sqrt{D} + (a_1 Q_1 - P_1)]}{D - (a_1 Q_1 - P_1)^2}} = a_1 + \frac{1}{\dfrac{\sqrt{D} + P_2}{Q_2}}$$

where $P_2 = a_1 Q_1 - P_1$ and

$$(1) \qquad Q_2 = \frac{D - P_2^2}{Q_1} = \frac{D - a_1^2 Q_1^2 + 2 a_1 Q_1 P_1 - P_1^2}{Q_1}$$

$$= \frac{D - P_1^2}{Q_1} - a_1^2 Q_1 + 2 a_1 P_1$$

Whether Q_2 is an integer depends upon $\dfrac{D - P_1^2}{Q_1}$ being an integer. If this function of the numbers in the original surd is not integral, then these numbers may be changed, without affecting the value of the surd, in such a way that the function will be an integer. That is, multiplication of both numerator and denominator of the surd by $|Q_1|$ gives

$$\frac{\sqrt{D} + P_1}{Q_1} = \frac{\sqrt{DQ_1^2} + P_1|Q_1|}{Q_1 \cdot |Q_1|} = \frac{\sqrt{\bar{D}} + \bar{P}}{\bar{Q}}.$$

In this surd,

$$\frac{\bar{D} - \bar{P}^2}{\bar{Q}} = \frac{DQ_1^2 - P_1^2 Q_1^2}{\pm Q_1^2} = \pm (D - P_1^2)$$

an integer.

Thus, when the expansion is begun, the surd may be assumed to be written in such a way that Q_2, when computed, will be integral. Note, also, from the first equality (1), that

$$\frac{D - P_2^2}{Q_2} = Q_1$$

is an integer.

Then, to complete the argument by induction, we define

$$\frac{\sqrt{D} + P_n}{Q_n} = a_n + \frac{1}{\dfrac{\sqrt{D} + P_{n+1}}{Q_{n+1}}}$$

in which $P_{n+1} = a_n Q_n - P_n$, and

$$(2) \qquad Q_{n+1} = \frac{D - P_{n+1}^2}{Q_n} = \frac{D - P_n^2}{Q_n} - a_n^2 Q_n + 2 a_n P_n$$

Assume $\dfrac{D - P_n^2}{Q_n}$ to be an integer. It follows that Q_{n+1} is an integer, and also from (2) that $\dfrac{D - P_{n+1}^2}{Q_{n+1}}$ is an integer. But we have already made Q_1, Q_2, $\dfrac{D - P_1^2}{Q_1}$, and $\dfrac{D - P_2^2}{Q_2}$ integers. Hence it follows that Q_i and $\dfrac{D - P_i^2}{Q_i}$ are integers for all values of i.

The complete quotients in the expansion of $\dfrac{\sqrt{D} + P}{Q}$ are therefore computed by the algorithm:

$$P_{n+1} = a_n Q_n - P_n$$

$$Q_{n+1} = \frac{D - P_{n+1}^2}{Q_n}$$

The computation is facilitated by the arrangement shown in the expansion of $\dfrac{\sqrt{30} - 2}{13}$. Note that $\dfrac{30 - 2^2}{13} = 2$, an integer.

$n:$	1	2	3	4	5	6	7
P	-2	2	4	3	3	4	4
Q	13	2	7	3	7	2	7
a	0	3	1	2	1	4	1

Since $x_7 = \dfrac{\sqrt{30}+4}{7}$ is identical with x_3, further expansion will repeat former terms.

Then $\dfrac{\sqrt{30}-2}{13} = (0, 3, \overline{1, 2, 1, 4})$.

EXERCISES IV

Find the continued fractions which represent:

1. $\sqrt{109}$.

2. $\dfrac{\sqrt{109}+7}{10}$.

3. $\dfrac{\sqrt{109}+12}{5}$.

4. $\dfrac{\sqrt{61}+7}{6}$.

5. $\dfrac{\sqrt{61}-7}{-6}$.

6. $\dfrac{\sqrt{61}+9}{4}$.

7. $\sqrt{u^2+1}$, u an integer.

8. $\sqrt{u^2+u}$, u an integer.

9. $\sqrt{u^2-2}$, u an integer.

10. $\sqrt{\dfrac{17}{3}}$.

11. $\sqrt{1633}$.

12. $\frac{1}{2} + \frac{1}{3}\sqrt{5}$.

We now prove:

THEOREM 15. *The simple continued fraction expansion of any quadratic surd is periodic.*

The method of proof will be to show that the P_i and Q_i can take but a limited number of values, which limits the number of possible complete quotients $\dfrac{\sqrt{D}+P_i}{Q_i}$; and when a complete quotient appears in the computation a second time the a_i begin to recur.

From algebra we recall some properties of functions involving quadratic surds. Let $\sqrt{z}$ be a pure quadratic surd in which z is an integer and not a square. Any rational function of $\sqrt{z}$ can be written in the form $a + b\sqrt{z}$, in which a and b are rational. If two such functions are equal, as

$$a + b\sqrt{z} = c + d\sqrt{z}$$

then $\qquad\qquad a = c \quad \text{and} \quad b = d$

Consequently, if the sign of $\sqrt{z}$ is changed in both functions, the equality is preserved, and

$$a - b\sqrt{z} = c - d\sqrt{z}$$

Thus, if, in any equation whose members are rational functions of a pure surd $\sqrt{z}$, the sign of $\sqrt{z}$ is changed throughout, the equality is preserved.

Now

(1) $$a_1 = x = \frac{p_{n-1}x_n + p_{n-2}}{q_{n-1}x_n + q_{n-2}} \qquad n > 2$$

in which $$x_n = \frac{\sqrt{D} + P_n}{Q_n}$$

Let $$y_n = \frac{-\sqrt{D} + P_n}{Q_n}$$

the conjugate surd of x_n. In (1) replace x_1 by y_1, x_n by y_n. This replacement is equivalent to changing the sign of $\sqrt{D}$ in each member of (1), since the p's and q's are rational. Then

(2) $$y_1 = \frac{p_{n-1}y_n + p_{n-2}}{q_{n-1}y_n + q_{n-2}}$$

Solving (2) for y_n, we get

$$y_n = -\frac{q_{n-2}y_1 - p_{n-2}}{q_{n-1}y_1 - p_{n-1}} = -\frac{q_{n-2}}{q_{n-1}} \cdot \frac{y_1 - \dfrac{p_{n-2}}{q_{n-2}}}{y_1 - \dfrac{p_{n-1}}{q_{n-1}}}$$

Now $$\lim_{n \to \infty} \frac{p_{n-2}}{q_{n-2}} = \lim_{n \to \infty} \frac{p_{n-1}}{q_{n-1}} = x_1$$

Hence $$\lim_{n \to \infty} \frac{y_1 - \dfrac{p_{n-2}}{q_{n-2}}}{y_1 - \dfrac{p_{n-1}}{q_{n-1}}} = 1$$

and we can write

$$y_n = -\frac{q_{n-2}}{q_{n-1}} (1 \pm \epsilon_n)$$

in which ϵ_n can be made arbitrarily small by taking n sufficiently large. Therefore, for sufficiently large n, y_n and also y_{n-1} are negative. We assume such a value of n.

Now, corresponding to $x_{n-1} = a_{n-1} + \dfrac{1}{x_n}$, we have $y_{n-1} =$

$a_{n-1} + \dfrac{1}{y_n}\cdot$ But $y_{n-1} < 0$, hence $\dfrac{1}{y_n} = y_{n-1} - a_{n-1} < -a_{n-1} \leqq -1$.

Then $\dfrac{1}{y_n} < -1$, and $-1 < y_n < 0$. Then since $x_n > 1$, both

expressions $x_n - y_n$ and $x_n + y_n$ are positive. That is

$$x_n - y_n = \frac{\sqrt{D} + P_n}{Q_n} - \frac{-\sqrt{D} + P_n}{Q_n} = \frac{2\sqrt{D}}{Q_n} > 0$$

hence $Q_n > 0$; and $x_n + y_n = \dfrac{2P_n}{Q_n} > 0$, which shows $P_n > 0$.

But $y_n = \dfrac{-\sqrt{D} + P_n}{Q_n} < 0$, hence $P_n < \sqrt{D}$.

Also $x_n = \dfrac{\sqrt{D} + P_n}{Q_n} > 1$, giving $Q_n < \sqrt{D} + P_n < 2\sqrt{D}$.

Thus we have found that $0 < P_n < \sqrt{D}$ and $0 < Q_n < 2\sqrt{D}$.

Therefore, after a certain point is reached in the expansion of x_1, the maximum number of values that x_n can take is $(2d + 1)d$, where d is the greatest integer in $\sqrt{D}$, and the periodicity is established.

20. Beginning of periodicity. We now discuss the point at which periodicity begins in the expansion of various types of quadratic surds.

Definitions. For this purpose we define a *reduced quadratic surd* x_1 as one in which $x_1 > 1$ and $-1 < y_1 < 0$.

Also a *purely periodic* simple continued fraction is one in which the periods begin with the first term. For example, the reduced quadratic surd $\dfrac{\sqrt{23} + 3}{7}$ expands into the purely periodic s.c.f.

$(\overline{1, 8, 1, 3})$. This illustrates:

THEOREM 16. *A reduced quadratic surd expands into a purely periodic simple continued fraction.*

We found above that, when $y_i < 0$, it follows that $-1 < y_{i+1} < 0$, and consequently all the y_i for a reduced surd lie between -1 and 0. Then since $y_i = a_i + \dfrac{1}{y_{i+1}}$, $-\dfrac{1}{y_{i+1}} = a_i - y_i$, and a_i is seen

to be the greatest integer in $-\dfrac{1}{y_{i+1}}\cdot$

Now suppose that the period includes the nth quotient, $n > 1$, and that there are k terms in a period, so that $x_n = x_{n+k}$, $y_n = y_{n+k}$. Then

$$-\frac{1}{y_n} = -\frac{1}{y_{n+k}}, \text{ and } a_{n-1} = a_{n-1+k}$$

Hence, since $x_{n-1} = a_{n-1} + \dfrac{1}{x_n}$ and $x_{n-1+k} = a_{n-1+k} + \dfrac{1}{x_{n+k}}$, we have

$$x_{n-1} = x_{n-1+k}$$

That is, from the occurrence of x_n in the period, follows the occurrence of x_{n-1}, and consequently of all preceding x_i, including x_1. Thus the fraction is purely periodic.

We now prove the converse:

THEOREM 17. *Any purely periodic simple continued fraction represents a reduced quadratic surd.*

Recall from the discussion of Theorem 14 that, if

$$x = (a_1, a_2, \cdots, a_k, x)$$

then

$$q_k x^2 + (q_{k-1} - p_k)x - p_{k-1} = 0$$

Since $a_1 = a_{k+1}$, we have $a_1 \geqq 1$ and $x > 1$. Let y be the conjugate of x; then $xy = -\dfrac{p_{k-1}}{q_k}$, and, since $x > 1$, $y < 0$.

Now the function $q_k x^2 + (q_{k-1} - p_k)x - p_{k-1} < 0$ for $x = 0$; and, for $x = -1$, it becomes $(q_k - q_{k-1}) + (p_k - p_{k-1}) > 0$. Hence the negative root of the equation lies between -1 and 0. Therefore, since $x > 1$ and $-1 < y < 0$, the surd is reduced.

As a further illustration, $\overline{(1, 2, 1)} = \dfrac{\sqrt{10} + 1}{3}$, a reduced surd.

Now assume a non-reduced surd in which $x_1 > 1$ but $y_1 < -1$. Then

$$y_1 = a_1 + \frac{1}{y_2} < -1, \quad \text{where} \quad a_1 \geqq 1$$

Or $\dfrac{1}{y_2} = y_1 - a_1 < -1$, hence $-1 < y_2 < 0$ and x_2 is a reduced surd. Therefore periodicity begins with the second term.

If any non-reduced surd has $x_1 < 1$, nevertheless $x_2 > 1$, as are all succeeding x_i. Hence the surd becomes reduced with the first term after x_1 for which $-1 < y_i < 0$, and periodicity begins at that point. By Theorem 17 periodicity cannot begin sooner. We summarize these results in:

THEOREM 18. *If* x_1 *is a quadratic surd, and* y_1 *its conjugate,* x_1 *will expand into a periodic simple continued fraction as follows:*

(1) When $x_1 > 1$ and $-1 < y_1 < 0$, the fraction is purely periodic.

(2) When $x_1 > 1$ and $y_1 < -1$, the fraction has just one non-periodic term.

(3) In all other cases the fraction has one or more non-periodic terms, and the first periodic term occurs at the first point after y_1 where $-1 < y_i < 0$.

In particular, the expansion of the pure surd $\sqrt{D}$ comes under part (2) of the theorem, for $\sqrt{D} > 1$ and $-\sqrt{D} < -1$.

THEOREM 19. *The last* Q_i *in each period of the expansion of* $\sqrt{\mathrm{D}}$ *is unity.*

By Theorem 18, (2), periodicity begins with the second term of the expansion. a_1 is the greatest integer in $\sqrt{D}$. Then, by the usual computation, $P_2 = a_1$ and $Q_2 = D - a_1^2$.

If k is the number of terms in a period, P_{k+2} and Q_{k+2} belong to the first term of the second period. Hence $P_{k+2} = a_1$ and $Q_{k+2} = D - a_1^2$. But·

$$D - P_{k+2}^2 = Q_{k+1}Q_{k+2}, \quad \text{then} \quad D - a_1^2 = Q_{k+1}(D - a_1^2)$$

Therefore $Q_{k+1} = 1$.

21. The equation $x^2 - Dy^2 = N$. We now derive the equation $p_n^2 - Dq_n^2 = (-1)^n Q_{n+1}$ which finds application in the solution of Diophantine equations of the form $x^2 - Dy^2 = N$ $(D > 0)$.

Expand $\sqrt{D}$, that is, put $P_1 = 0$ and $Q_1 = 1$, and we have

$$x_1 = \sqrt{D} = \frac{p_{n-1}x_n + p_{n-2}}{q_{n-1}x_n + q_{n-2}}.$$

In this put $$x_n = \frac{\sqrt{D} + P_n}{Q_n}$$

and get $$\sqrt{D} = \frac{p_{n-1}\sqrt{D} + p_{n-1}P_n + p_{n-2}Q_n}{q_{n-1}\sqrt{D} + q_{n-1}P_n + q_{n-2}Q_n}$$

Clearing this of fractions and equating to zero separately the coefficient of $\sqrt{D}$ and the terms free from $\sqrt{D}$, we get

$$q_{n-1}P_n + q_{n-2}Q_n = p_{n-1}$$

$$p_{n-1}P_n + p_{n-2}Q_n = q_{n-1}D$$

The elimination of P_n between these gives

$$(p_{n-1}q_{n-2} - p_{n-2}q_{n-1})Q_n = p_{n-1}^2 - q_{n-1}^2 D$$

or
$$(-1)^{n-1}Q_n = p_{n-1}^2 - q_{n-1}^2 D$$

Writing n for $n - 1$,

$$p_n^2 - q_n^2 D = (-1)^n Q_{n+1}$$

This equation makes possible the solution of $x^2 - Dy^2 = N$ ($D > 0$) if, for some value of n, $(-1)^n Q_{n+1} = N$.

Example. In solving $x^2 - 58y^2 = N$ we expand $\sqrt{58}$ into a continued fraction getting

n	1	2	3	4	5	6	7	8
P	0	7	2	4	3	4	2	7
Q	1	9	6	7	7	6	9	1
a	7	1	1	1	1	1	1	14

Then compute p_i and q_i.

n		1	2	3	4	5	6	7	8	9	10
a		7	1	1	1	1	1	1	14	1	1
p	0	1	7	8	15	23	38	61	99	1447	1546	2993
q	1	0	1	1	2	3	5	8	13	190	203	393

n	11	12	13	14
a	1	1	1	1
p	4539	7532	12071	19603
q	596	989	1585	2574

We shall consider the special values $N = 9$, $N = -1$, $N = +1$.

Solution of $x^2 - 58y^2 = 9$. Since N is positive, n is even, and 9 must be a Q_i of odd order. From the above $Q_7 = 9$. Then $x = p_6 = 61$, $y = q_6 = 8$ gives one solution. In fact $61^2 - 58 \cdot 8^2 = 3721 - 3712 = 9$. Since the number of terms in the period is odd, this value of Q_i recurs with an odd subscript in alternating periods. That is,

$$Q_7 = Q_{21} = Q_{35} = \cdots = 9$$

and an infinite number of solutions is represented by $x = p_{6+14t}$, $y = q_{6+14t}$. Also $Q_2 = 9 = Q_{9+14t}$, and we have the additional solutions $x = p_{8+14t}$, $y = q_{8+14t}$.

Solution of $x^2 - 58y^2 = -1$.

$$Q_8 = 1, \quad \text{and} \quad x = p_7 = 99, \quad y = q_7 = 13$$

In general, $\qquad\qquad x = p_{7+14t}, \quad y = q_{7+14t}$

Solution of $x^2 - 58y^2 = 1$. Here n is even, and to find a Q_i of suitable order we take Q_{8+7}, hence

$$x = p_{14+14t}, \quad y = q_{14+14t}$$

For $t = 0$, $x = p_{14} = 19,603$, $y = q_{14} = 2574$.

The equation $x^2 - Dy^2 = 1$ *may always be solved by the above method.* For, by Theorem 19, the last Q_i of each period is unity. Then, if the number of terms, k, in the period is even, $Q_{k+1} = 1$ is of odd order and $(-1)^k Q_{k+1} = 1$. If the number of terms in the period is odd, Q_{2k+1} is of odd order and $(-1)^{2k} Q_{2k+1} = 1$. Hence in the first case, $x = p_k, y = q_k$, and in the second, $x = p_{2k}, y = q_{2k}$.

When one solution of the equation is known, infinitely many others may be gotten as follows, without the use of the continued fraction expansion. Let $x = p$, $y = q$ be one solution. Then

$$x^2 - Dy^2 = (p^2 - Dq^2)^n = 1$$

or $\quad (x + \sqrt{D}y)(x - \sqrt{D}y) = (p + \sqrt{D}q)^n (p - \sqrt{D}q)^n$

This equation will be satisfied by putting

$$x + \sqrt{D}y = (p + \sqrt{D}q)^n$$

and $\qquad\qquad x - \sqrt{D}y = (p - \sqrt{D}q)^n$

By adding and subtracting we get

$$x = \tfrac{1}{2}\left[(p + \sqrt{D}q)^n + (p - \sqrt{D}q)^n\right]$$

$$y = \frac{1}{2\sqrt{D}}\left[(p + \sqrt{D}q)^n - (p - \sqrt{D}q)^n\right]$$

Then, by giving different values to n, any number of solutions may be obtained.*

The equation $x^2 - Dy^2 = -1$ *may be solved if there is an odd number of terms in the period of the expansion of* $\sqrt{D}$.

For, since k is odd, $(-1)^k Q_{k+1} = -1$.

Again, let $x = p$, $y = q$ be one solution, then an arbitrary number of solutions may be obtained as follows. We have

$$x^2 - Dy^2 = (p^2 - Dq^2)^{2n-1} = -1$$

or $(x + \sqrt{D}y)(x - \sqrt{D}y) = (p + \sqrt{D}q)^{2n-1}(p - \sqrt{D}q)^{2n-1}$

which is satisfied by putting

$$x + \sqrt{D}y = (p + \sqrt{D}q)^{2n-1}$$

$$x - \sqrt{D}y = (p - \sqrt{D}q)^{2n-1}$$

From these

$$x = \tfrac{1}{2}[(p + \sqrt{D}q)^{2n-1} + (p - \sqrt{D}q)^{2n-1}]$$

$$y = \frac{1}{2\sqrt{D}}[(p + \sqrt{D}q)^{2n-1} - (p - \sqrt{D}q)^{2n-1}]$$

To illustrate, solve $x^2 - 13y^2 = -1$.

$$\sqrt{13} = (3, \overline{1, 1, 1, 1, 6})$$

in which $k = 5$, and $(-1)^k Q_{k+1} = -1$. Then one solution is $x = p_5 = 18$, $y = q_5 = 5$. Using this solution in the general formula, and putting $n = 2$, we get

$$x = \tfrac{1}{2}[(18 + \sqrt{13 \cdot 5})^3 + (18 - \sqrt{13 \cdot 5})^3] = 23{,}382$$

$$y = \frac{1}{2\sqrt{13}}[(18 + \sqrt{13 \cdot 5})^3 - (18 - \sqrt{13 \cdot 5})^3] = 6485$$

Similarly, general formulas giving an infinite number of solutions of the equation $x^2 - Dy^2 = N$ are derived as follows, when one solution is known.

Let $x = h$, $y = k$ be a solution of $x^2 - Dy^2 = 1$ and $x = p$,

---

* It can be shown that the solutions given by these formulas are the same as those given by using the various periods of the continued fraction. See Perron, "Die Lehre von den Kettenbruchen," p. 104.

$y = q$ a known solution of $x^2 - Dy^2 = $ N. Then, since $h^2 - Dk^2 = 1$.

$$N = x^2 - Dy^2 = (p^2 - Dq^2)(h^2 - Dk^2) = (ph \pm Dqk)^2 - D(pk \pm qh)^2$$

from which we get

$$x = ph \pm Dqk$$

$$y = pk \pm qh$$

If p and q are fixed, infinitely many solutions are obtained by letting h and k run through all possible solutions of $x^2 - Dy^2 = 1$. We shall see below that the continued fraction expansion gives all possible solutions of the latter. But the general formulas just derived from a single solution of $x^2 - Dy^2 = N$ do not necessarily give all solutions as we see from the example $x^2 - 21y^2 = 60$. Two solutions of this equation are $x = 9, y = 1$ and $x = 12, y = 2$. When one of these is substituted for x and y and the other for p and q in the formulas it is readily found by simultaneous solution that h and k cannot be integers. Hence one of the solutions cannot be obtained from the other by using integral values of h and k. However, the following theorem shows that the continued fraction expansion affords a method of finding all solutions of the equation when $| N | < \sqrt{D}$.

THEOREM 20. *If* x = p, y = q *are positive integers satisfying the equation* $x^2 - Dy^2 = $ N, *where* $| N | < \sqrt{D}$, *then* p/q *is a convergent in the s.c.f. expansion of* $\sqrt{D}$.

First we assume $N > 0$.
From $p^2 - Dq^2 = N$ we write

$$(p - \sqrt{D}q)(p + \sqrt{D}q) = N$$

and

$$\frac{p}{q} - \sqrt{D} = \frac{N}{q(p + \sqrt{D}q)}$$

Then, since $0 < N < \sqrt{D}$, it follows that

$$0 < \frac{p}{q} - \sqrt{D} < \frac{\sqrt{D}}{q(p + \sqrt{D}q)}$$

and

$$0 < \frac{p}{q} - \sqrt{D} < \frac{1}{q^2 \left(\dfrac{p}{q\sqrt{D}} + 1 \right)}$$

But from $\dfrac{p}{q} - \sqrt{D} > 0$, we have $\dfrac{p}{q\sqrt{D}} > 1$ and $\dfrac{p}{q\sqrt{D}} + 1 > 2.$

Combining these inequalities we get

$$0 < \frac{p}{q} - \sqrt{D} < \frac{1}{2q^2}$$

or

$$\left| \frac{p}{q} - \sqrt{D} \right| < \frac{1}{2q^2}$$

And by using Theorem 13 the argument for $N > 0$ is completed. For use in the following we note that nothing in the proof requires that D and N be integers.

In case $N < 0$ we rewrite the equation $p^2 - Dq^2 = N$ in the form $q^2 - p^2 \dfrac{1}{D} = -\dfrac{N}{D}$ in which $\dfrac{-N}{D} > 0$. This is of the form of the first equation with D and N replaced by $\dfrac{1}{D}$ and $\dfrac{-N}{D}$ respectively. By the above proof $\dfrac{q}{p}$ is a convergent in the expansion of $\dfrac{1}{\sqrt{D}}$ if $\left| \dfrac{-N}{D} \right| < \dfrac{1}{\sqrt{D}}$. But this is equivalent to the given condition $|N| < \sqrt{D}$. Hence $\dfrac{q}{p}$ is such a convergent. Then, by Exercises I, 12, $\dfrac{p}{q}$ is a convergent in the expansion of $\sqrt{D}$.

It follows directly that all solutions of $x^2 - Dy^2 = N$, *where* $|N| < \sqrt{D}$, *are among the convergents of the s.c.f. expansion of* $\sqrt{D}$. *In particular the equation for* $N = -1$ *has no solution if the number of terms in the period of the s.c.f. is even.*

EXERCISES V

Solve the equations:

1. $x^2 - 29y^2 = \pm 1.$ 3. $x^2 - 76y^2 = \pm 1.$
2. $x^2 - 86y^2 = \pm 1.$ 4. $x^2 - 53y^2 = \pm 4.$
5. Find the prime factors of 1819 by solving the equation $x^2 - 1819y^2 = 9.$

6. Derive the equation $vp_n^2 - uq_n^2 = (-1)^n Q_{n+1}$ from the expansion of $\sqrt{\dfrac{u}{v}}$.

Find two solutions if possible for each equation:

7. $5x^2 - 13y^2 = \pm 8$.   **8.** $3x^2 - 17y^2 = 7$.

9. Find a solution of $x^2 - (a^2 - 2)y^2 = 3 - 2a$.

10. Write out the general solution of $x^2 - 7y^2 = 1$, and from it compute two specific solutions.

Chapter III

CONGRUENCES

22. Definitions. *If* a − b *is divisible by* m > 0, *we say that* a *is congruent to* b *modulo* m. This is written $a \equiv b$ (mod m), or simply $a \equiv b$, if the modulus m is implied in the context. For example, the difference of any two of the numbers 11, 26, 71, −4 is divisible by 15, and we write $11 \equiv 71$ (mod 15), $26 \equiv -4$ (mod 15), etc.

Similarly *if* a − b *is not divisible by* m, *we say that* a *is incongruent to* b *modulo* m and write $a \not\equiv b$ (mod m).

From the above definitions the congruence $a \equiv b$ (mod m) and the equation $a = b + qm$ are seen to be equivalent relationships.

Although the special notation for congruence is thus in a way redundant, its invention by Gauss proved a stroke of genius which has stimulated great advances in the development of the theory of numbers.

As a second definition we say that $a \equiv b$ (mod m) *when, and only when, the remainders obtained in dividing* a *and* b *by* m *are the same.* To see that this is equivalent to the first definition, we put $a = q_1 m + r_1$ and $b = q_2 m + r_2$, where r_1 and r_2 are zero or positive and $< m$. Then $a - b = (q_1 - q_2)m + r_1 - r_2$ with $|r_1 - r_2| < m$. Hence the condition that $a - b$ is a multiple of m is equivalent to the condition that $r_1 = r_2$. That is, since $71 = 4 \cdot 15 + 11$ and $-4 = -1 \cdot 15 + 11$ we have $71 \equiv -4$ (mod 15).

This defining of congruence in terms of remainders gives rise to the concept of *residues*. In general, if two numbers are congruent to each other, either is said to be a residue of the other.

23. Fundamentals. The following theorems follow readily from these definitions of a congruence.

THEOREM 1. *If* a $\equiv$ b (*mod* m), *then* ac $\equiv$ bc (*mod* mc).

For, since $a - b = qm$, it follows that $ac - bc = qmc$, and $ac \equiv bc$ (mod mc).

THEOREM 2. *If* a $\equiv$ b (*mod* m), *and if* d *is any divisor of* m, *then* a $\equiv$ b (*mod* d).

This is a direct consequence of the first definition of a congruence.

THEOREM 3. *If* $a \equiv b$ *(mod* m_1*),* $a \equiv b$ *(mod* m_2*),* $\cdots$, $a \equiv b$ *(mod* m_k*), where the* m_i *are relatively prime in pairs, then* $a \equiv b$ *(mod* $m_1 \cdot m_2 \cdots m_k$*).*

For since $a - b$ is divisible by each of the relatively prime integers m_i it is divisible by their product.

THEOREM 4. *If* $a \equiv b$ *(mod* m*) and* $b \equiv c$ *(mod* m*), then* $a \equiv c$ *(mod* m*).*

For, since $a - b = q_1 m$ and $b - c = q_2 m$, by addition we have $a - c = (q_1 + q_2)m$.

From this it follows directly that all integers may be arranged in classes with reference to a modulus m. We define a *number class* modulo m as *the totality of integers each of which is congruent to a given integer modulo* m. Consequently any two integers of a number class are congruent to each other. It appears at once that no integer can belong to more than one number class modulo m. Also each number class contains one and only one positive integer $\leqq m$. Thus all integers are arranged in just m number classes modulo m, and any integer defines the class to which it belongs and represents that class with reference to the modulus.

Any set of m integers such that no two of them belong to the same number class is said to form a *complete system of incongruent numbers,* or a *complete residue system modulo* m. For example, such a residue system modulo 5 is 4, 6, 13, 10, 2. Each of these numbers represents one of the five number classes modulo 5. The smallest positive, or zero, residues representing these number classes in the same order are 4, 1, 3, 0, 2. Such a set we call a *complete system of least non-negative residues.* Another complete set of residues, particularly useful for computational purposes, is *the complete set of numerically least residues,* which for the modulus 5 in the same order as the above set is -1, 1, -2, 0, 2.

THEOREM 5. *If* $a \equiv b$ *(mod* m*) and* $c \equiv d$ *(mod* m*), then* $a \pm c \equiv b \pm d$ *(mod* m*).*

For, since $a - b = q_1 m$ and $c - d = q_2 m$, we have

$$(a - b) \pm (c - d) = (q_1 \pm q_2)m$$

or $$(a + c) - (b + d) = (q_1 + q_2)m$$

and $$(a - c) - (b - d) = (q_1 - q_2)m$$

Therefore $$a + c \equiv b + d, \text{ and } a - c \equiv b - d$$

For example, since $30 \equiv 8 \pmod{11}$ and $13 \equiv 2 \pmod{11}$, then $43 \equiv 10$ and $17 \equiv 6$.

THEOREM 6. *If* $a \equiv b \pmod{m}$ *and* $c \equiv d \pmod{m}$, *then* $ac \equiv bd \pmod{m}$.

For, since $a - b$ and $c - d$ are multiples of m, $(a - b)c + b(c - d) = ac - bd$ is a multiple of m and $ac \equiv bd \pmod{m}$.

For example, since $15 \equiv 2 \pmod{13}$ and $5 \equiv 18 \pmod{13}$, then $75 \equiv 36$.

COROLLARY. *In particular, if* $a \equiv b \pmod{m}$, *then* $a^n \equiv b^n \pmod{m}$, *where* n *is a positive integer.*

As an immediate consequence of these theorems we can state:

THEOREM 7. *If* $a_i \equiv b_i \pmod{m}$ *and* $x_j \equiv y_j \pmod{m}$, *then any polynomial in the* x_j *with the* a_i *for coefficients is congruent modulo* m *to the similarly formed polynomial in the* y_j *with the* b_i *for coefficients.*

For example,

$$25x_1^3 - 115x_2x_3^2 + 98x_1x_2 \equiv 3y_1^3 - 5y_2y_3^2 - y_1y_2 \pmod{11}$$

whenever $\qquad x_1 \equiv y_1, \ x_2 \equiv y_2, \ x_3 \equiv y_3 \pmod{11}$

THEOREM 8A. *If* $a \equiv b \pmod{m}$, *with* d *as any common divisor of* a *and* b, *and* $(m, d) = g$, *then* $\dfrac{a}{d} \equiv \dfrac{b}{d} \left(mod \ \dfrac{m}{g} \right)$.

For, from $a - b = mt$, we have $\left(\dfrac{a}{d} - \dfrac{b}{d} \right)\dfrac{d}{g} = \dfrac{m}{g} \cdot t$ with $\left(\dfrac{d}{g}, \dfrac{m}{g} \right) = 1$. Hence $\dfrac{m}{g}$ divides $\dfrac{a}{d} - \dfrac{b}{d}$, and $\dfrac{a}{d} \equiv \dfrac{b}{d} \left(mod \ \dfrac{m}{g} \right)$.

Example: $144 \equiv 66 \pmod{39}$.

Here 6 is a common divisor of 144 and 66, also $(39, 6) = 3$. Then from the given congruence by this theorem we have $24 \equiv 11 \pmod{13}$. Note that $24 \equiv 11 \pmod{39}$ is false, as also is $48 \equiv 22 \pmod{39}$. But by Theorem 8A we may write $72 \equiv 33 \pmod{39}$.

COROLLARY: *In particular, if* $a \equiv b \pmod{m}$, *with* d *any common divisor of* a *and* b, *and* $(m, d) = 1$, *then* $\dfrac{a}{d} \equiv \dfrac{b}{d} \pmod{m}$.

Example: Since $36 \equiv 15 \pmod{7}$, and $(7, 3) = 1$, then $12 \equiv 5 \pmod{7}$.

THEOREM 8B. *If* a ≡ b *(mod* m), *then* (a, m) = (b, m).

For from the congruence we have $a = b + mt$. From this it follows that any number which divides m and either of the numbers a or b must divide the other. In particular we note that, if $(a, m) = 1$, then $(b, m) = 1$, and vice versa.

This completes the statement of the fundamental theorems governing the usual operations with congruences. A limited analogy with the corresponding operations with equations is evident. The fact that Gauss's notation sets forth this analogy clearly is one weighty reason for its importance.

The complete set of least residues modulo m contains $\phi(m)$ numbers prime to m. It follows then from Theorem 8B that any complete residue system contains just $\phi(m)$ integers prime to m. Such a set of $\phi(m)$ integers is called a *reduced residue system modulo* m. A reduced residue system modulo 10 is 11, 13, 17, 9.

THEOREM 9. *If* x *takes all the values of a complete residue system modulo* m, *and if* (a, m) = 1, *then* ax + b *also takes the values of a complete residue system modulo* m.

In particular, any arithmetic progression of m integers, in which the common difference is prime to m, forms a complete residue system modulo m.

We prove this by showing that no two of the values of $ax + b$, obtained by putting $x = x_1$ and x_2, are congruent. Suppose

$$ax_1 + b \equiv ax_2 + b$$

Then $$a(x_1 - x_2) \equiv 0$$

and, since $(a, m) = 1$, we would have $x_1 \equiv x_2$, which is contrary to hypothesis. Therefore

$$ax_1 + b \not\equiv ax_2 + b$$

EXERCISES I

Find one value of x which satisfies:

1. $150x + 45 \equiv 0$ (mod 11).
2. $462x - 731 \equiv 0$ (mod 13).
3. Prove that, if $ab \equiv cd$ (mod m), $b \equiv d$ (mod m), and $(b, m) = 1$, then $a \equiv c$ (mod m).
4. Show that any integer is congruent to the sum of its digits modulo 9.
5. State and prove a similar proposition for modulus 11.
6. Show that $(a + b)^p \equiv a^p + b^p$ (mod p), where p is a prime.

7. Tabulate the values of $5x + 2$ obtained by letting $x = 0, 1, 2, \cdots, 11$. Show, by reducing them to their least positive residues modulo 12, that they form a complete residue system.

Do the same for $7x + 3$.

8. Give a second proof of Theorem **7**, Chapter I: $\phi(mn) = \phi(m)\phi(n)$ when $(m, n) = 1$.

Suggestion: $nx + b$ will take all values $0, 1, 2, 3, \cdots, mn - 1$ as we put $b = 0, 1, 2, \cdots, n - 1$ and $x = 0, 1, 2, \cdots, m - 1$.

If b_1 is a value of b prime to n, then $\phi(m)$ numbers of the arithmetic progression $nx + b_1$ are prime to both m and n.

9. Show that the congruence $x^2 \equiv 3 \pmod 7$ has no solution.

10. Prove that, if each of the $\phi(m)$ numbers of a reduced residue system modulo m is multiplied by a number prime to m, then the products form a reduced residue system modulo m.

11. Arrange the numbers $2, 3, 4, \cdots, 15$ in pairs, a and b, such that for each pair $ab \equiv 1 \pmod{17}$.

24. Fermat's theorem. THEOREM 10. *If* p *is a prime and* $(a, p) = 1$, *then* $a^{p-1} \equiv 1$ *(mod* p*).* (Compare with Exercise 12, page 14).

The numbers ax, where $x = 1, 2, \cdots, p - 1$, are congruent in some order to the numbers $1, 2, \cdots, p - 1$. Therefore

$$a \cdot 2a \cdot 3a \cdot 4a \cdots (p - 1)a \equiv 1 \cdot 2 \cdot 3 \cdot 4 \cdots (p - 1) \pmod p$$

Or $\qquad\qquad a^{p-1}(p - 1)! \equiv (p - 1)!$

But $\qquad\qquad ((p - 1)!, p) = 1$

Hence $\qquad\qquad a^{p-1} \equiv 1$

Since a can be any integer prime to p, it can take $p - 1$ incongruent values. This is equivalent to saying that *the congruence*

$$x^{p-1} - 1 \equiv 0 \pmod p$$

where p *is a prime, has just* p $- 1$ *incongruent roots.*

COROLLARY. *If* p *is an odd prime and not a divisor of* a, *then either*

$$a^{\frac{1}{2}(p-1)} \equiv 1 \pmod p \quad \text{or} \quad a^{\frac{1}{2}(p-1)} \equiv -1 \pmod p$$

This follows by writing

$$a^{p-1} - 1 = (a^{\frac{1}{2}(p-1)} - 1)(a^{\frac{1}{2}(p-1)} + 1) \equiv 0 \pmod p$$

THEOREM 11 (*Euler's generalization of Fermat's theorem*). **If** $(a, m) = 1$ *and* m > 0, *then* $a^{\phi(m)} \equiv 1$ *(mod* m*).*

Let $n_1, n_2, n_3, \cdots, n_{\phi(m)}$ be *a reduced residue system* of numbers $\leqq m$ and prime to it. Then $an_1, an_2, an_3, \cdots, an_{\phi(m)}$ is also a reduced residue system modulo m. Hence by Theorem 6 we write

$$an_1 \cdot an_2 \cdots an_{\phi(m)} \equiv n_1 \cdot n_2 \cdots n_{\phi(m)} \ (\text{mod } m)$$

or $\qquad\qquad a^{\phi(m)} \, \Pi n_i \equiv \Pi n_i \ (\text{mod } m)$

But $\qquad\qquad\quad (\Pi n_i, m) = 1$

Therefore $\qquad\qquad a^{\phi(m)} \equiv 1 \ (\text{mod } m)$

Since, in this result, a is necessarily prime to m, it follows that the congruence

$$x^{\phi(m)} \equiv 1 \ (\text{mod } m)$$

has just $\phi(m)$ incongruent solutions.

The direct converse of Fermat's theorem would be: *Given* $a^{n-1} \equiv 1$ *(mod* n), *then* n *is a prime.* Clearly this is not a true proposition, since we may take $a \equiv 1 \ (\text{mod } n)$. A less trivial example of its failure is $4^{14} = (4^2)^7 = 16^7 \equiv 1 \ (\text{mod } 15)$, and 15 is not a prime. However, by including another condition in the hypothesis, a modified converse may be stated and proved as follows.

THEOREM 12. *If* $a^{n-1} \equiv 1$ *(mod* n), *where* (a, n) = 1, *and* $a^g \not\equiv 1$ *(mod* n) *for* g *any divisor of* n − 1 *and less than* n − 1, *then* n *is a prime.*

Assume n to be composite. Then $\phi(n) < n - 1$. Let $(\phi(n), n - 1) = g$. By Theorem 2, Chapter I, x and y can be found so that $g = \phi(n)x + (n - 1)y$. Since $0 < g < n - 1$, one of x and y will be positive and the other negative.

Assume $x < 0$ and $y > 0$.

Now by Theorem 11 $a^{\phi(n)} \equiv 1 \ (\text{mod } n)$ and by hypothesis $a^{n-1} \equiv 1 \ (\text{mod } n)$. Hence $a^{|x| \cdot \phi(n)} \equiv 1 \ (\text{mod } n)$ and $a^{y(n-1)} \equiv 1 \ (\text{mod } n)$. Applying Exercises I, 3 to these congruences, we may write

$$a^{x \cdot \phi(n)} \cdot a^{y(n-1)} \equiv a^{x \cdot \phi(n) + y(n-1)} \equiv a^g \equiv 1 \ (\text{mod } n)$$

which is contrary to hypothesis.

Similarly this result may be obtained when $x > 0$ and $y < 0$.

Therefore the assumption that n is composite is false and n is prime.

Note that in the example $4^{14} \equiv 1$ (mod 15) the condition that $a^g \not\equiv 1$ (mod 15) fails for $g = 2$ since $4^2 \equiv 1$ (mod 15).

25. Wilson's theorem. THEOREM 13. *If* p *is a prime, then* $(p - 1)! + 1 \equiv 0$ *(mod* p).

If both a and b are limited to the values 1, 2, 3, $\cdots$, $(p - 1)$, then it follows from Theorem 9, or from Exercise 10 above, that there is just one value of each for a given value of the other which makes $ab \equiv 1$ (mod p). Thus the numbers 1, 2, 3, $\cdots$, $(p - 1)$ are arranged in pairs such that the product of the numbers of a pair is congruent to 1 modulo p.

If the members of a pair are equal, we have $a^2 \equiv 1$ or $(a + 1)(a - 1) \equiv 0$, and p divides either $a + 1$ or $a - 1$. Hence either $a \equiv -1 \equiv p - 1$ or $a \equiv 1$, and 1 and $p - 1$ are the only numbers of the set for which this can occur. Hence with the remaining numbers of the set we can write

$$2 \cdot 3 \cdot 4 \cdots (p - 2) \equiv 1$$

and $$(p - 1)! \equiv p - 1 \equiv -1 \ (\text{mod } p)$$

EXERCISES II

1. Show that $x^{13} - x \equiv 0$ (mod 2730) for all values of x.

2. State and prove the converse of Wilson's theorem.

3. Prove that $n^6 - 1 \equiv 0$ (mod 504), when n is not divisible by 2, 3, or 7.

4. For what values of n is $n^{12} - 1 \equiv 0$ (mod 65,520)?

5. Show that, if p and q are different primes, $p^{q-1} + q^{p-1} - 1 \equiv 0$ (mod pq).

6. If p is a prime of the form $4n + 1$, show that $\left| \frac{1}{2}(p - 1) \right.$ is a solution of the congruence $x^2 + 1 \equiv 0$ (mod p). *Suggestion:* Note that $p - k \equiv - k$ (mod p).

7. If p is a prime of the form $4n - 1$, show that $\left| \frac{1}{2}(p - 1) \right.$ is a solution of the congruence $x^2 - 1 \equiv 0$ (mod p).

8. Prove Fermat's theorem by showing that

$$(x_1 + x_2 + x_3 + \cdots + x_a)^p \equiv x_1^p + x_2^p + \cdots + x_a^p \ (\text{mod } p)$$

and putting each $x_i = 1$.

9. Prove that, if d is the least value of $x > 0$ for which $a^x \equiv 1$ (mod m), where $(a, m) = 1$, then d is a divisor of $\phi(m)$. *Suggestion:* Assume $\phi(m) = qd + r$, where $0 \leqq r < d$, and use Fermat's theorem.

10. Prove that, if d is the least value of $x > 0$ for which $a^x \equiv b^x$ (mod p), where p is a prime which does not divide a or b, then $p - 1 \equiv 0$ (mod d).

11. Use Exercise 10 to find the factors of $3^{11} - 1 = 177,146$.

12. Show that $2^{16} + 1 = 65,537$ is a prime.

Use Fermat's theorem to find a value of x which will satisfy the congruence:

13. $7x \equiv 1 \pmod{19}$.   **15.** $43x \equiv 7 \pmod{96}$.

14. $13x \equiv 11 \pmod{29}$.   **16.** $86x \equiv 14 \pmod{96}$.

17. Prove that x^5 has the same right-hand digit as x, where x is any integer.

18. Prove that x^9 has one of the forms $19n$, $19n \pm 1$, where x is any integer.

19. Show that $18! + 1 \equiv 0 \pmod{437}$.

20. Show that $2(p - 3)! + 1 \equiv 0 \pmod{p}$, where p is an odd prime.

21. Prove that, if $m^p + n^p \equiv 0 \pmod{p}$, then $m^p + n^p \equiv 0 \pmod{p^2}$, where p is an odd prime.

26. Roots of congruence. Congruences involving unknown quantities have already entered into our discussion. In particular we noticed that the Fermat theorem means that any number prime to p satisfies the congruence $x^{p-1} \equiv 1 \pmod{p}$. Likewise, from the generalization of this theorem, we know that any number prime to m satisfies the congruence $x^{\phi(m)} \equiv 1 \pmod{m}$. A number which satisfies a congruence when substituted for a variable occurring therein is called a root of the congruence. Clearly, if x_1 is a root of a congruence having the modulus m, the infinitely many integers of the number class $x_1 + mt$ are also roots. Two integers of this number class are not regarded as distinct roots. We may then speak of a number class as satisfying the congruence. Thus the number of roots of a congruence means the number of number classes with respect to the modulus which satisfy the congruence. Then the congruence $x^{p-1} \equiv 1 \pmod{p}$ has $p - 1$ roots, and $x^{\phi(m)} \equiv 1 \pmod{m}$ has $\phi(m)$ roots. We now address ourselves to the problem of solving certain congruences.

27. Linear congruences. The general linear congruence in one variable may be written $ax \equiv b \pmod{m}$.

First we assume $(a, m) = 1$. Then by Theorem 9, as x takes the values of a complete residue system modulo m, ax also runs through m incongruent values. Hence ax will be congruent to b for just one value of x, and *the congruence has just one root.*

This root may be found by writing the congruence in the form of the Diophantine equation $ax - my = b$, and solving the equation by either of the methods already given. Or the root may be written out by means of Fermat's theorem. That is, $x = a^{\phi(m)-1} \cdot b$, for $a \cdot (a^{\phi(m)-1} \cdot b) \equiv a^{\phi(m)} \cdot b \equiv b \pmod{m}$.

Example: Solve $14x \equiv 9 \pmod{15}$.

$$\phi(15) = 8. \quad \text{Hence} \quad x \equiv 14^7 \cdot 9$$

Since $14^2 \equiv 1$, $14^7 \equiv 14$, and $x \equiv 6$,

However, the solution can be readily found in many cases by inspection and trial, facilitated by suitable changes in the coefficients of the congruence.

For example, solve $36x \equiv 7 \pmod{157}$.

We have $\qquad 36x \equiv -150, \quad$ or $\quad 6x \equiv -25$

and $\qquad\qquad 6x \equiv 132, \quad$ or $\quad x \equiv 22$

Again, solve $7x \equiv 15 \pmod{40}$.

Since 7 is prime to $5 = (15, 40)$, x must be a multiple of 5, say $5y$. Then

$$7 \cdot 5y \equiv 15 \pmod{40}$$

$$7y \equiv 3 \pmod{8}$$

$$-y \equiv 3 \pmod{8}$$

$$y \equiv -3 \equiv 5 \pmod{8}$$

and $\qquad\qquad x = 5y \equiv 25$

We now proceed to prove the theorem concerning the number of solutions of the general linear congruence in one unknown.

THEOREM 14. *The congruence*

$$(1) \qquad\qquad ax \equiv b \pmod{m}$$

where $(a, m) = d$, *has no solutions or exactly* d *solutions, according as* b *is not, or is, a multiple of* d.

When the congruence is written in the form $ax - my = b$, it is evident that any common divisor of a and m must divide b also. This proves the first part of the theorem.

Also, we have proved the theorem for $d = 1$.

We now assume that $d > 1$, and b is a multiple of d. Let $a = a'd$, $b = b'd$, and $m = m'd$. Then by Theorem 8A we write

$$(2) \qquad\qquad a'x \equiv b' \pmod{m'}$$

in which $(a', m') = 1$. Clearly, any value of x which satisfies either (1) or (2) satisfies the other. Now (2) has just one solution, the number class $x_1 + m'y$. But the numbers of this class modulo m' are not all congruent modulo m. Putting $y = 1, 2, \cdots, d - 1$, we get the d numbers

$$x_1, \; x_1 + m', \; x_1 + 2m', \; \cdots, \; x_1 + (d - 1)m'$$

which are incongruent to each other modulo m. Also any other value of y would give a root congruent to one of these modulo $m = dm'$. Hence, in this case, there are just d distinct roots of (1).

Example: Solve

(1) $95x \equiv 90 \pmod{115}$

Here $(95, 115) = 5$, and we write

(2) $19x \equiv 18 \pmod{23}$

The solution of (2) is $x = 7 + 23y$. Giving y the values 0, 1, 2, 3, 4, we get

$$x \equiv 7, 30, 53, 76, 99$$

as the distinct solutions of (1).

EXERCISES III

Solve the congruences:

1. $350x \equiv 487 \pmod{729}$.   **3.** $16x \equiv 24 \pmod{64}$.
2. $39x \equiv 129 \pmod{42}$.   **4.** $900x \equiv 7 \pmod{589}$.

Determine the number of solutions of each of the congruences:

5. $43x \equiv 7 \pmod{96}$.   **6.** $44x \equiv 14 \pmod{96}$.   **7.** $60x \equiv 120 \pmod{720}$.

28. Linear congruences, more than one unknown. We now consider briefly *linear congruences in more than one variable.*

THEOREM 15. *The congruence* $ax + by + c \equiv 0$ *(mod m) has no solutions* (x, y) *or* dm *solutions according as* c *is not or is divisible by* d. *Here* $d = (a, b, m)$.

Obviously c must contain d as a factor if any solutions of

(1) $ax + by + c \equiv 0 \pmod{m}$

exist. Then, dividing through the congruence, including the modulus, by d, we get

(2) $a'x + b'y + c' \equiv 0 \pmod{m'}$

in which $(a', b', m') = 1$.

Now let $(a', m') = d'$; then, if (2) has solutions,

(3) $b'y + c' \equiv 0 \pmod{d'}$

But, since $(b', d') = 1$, (3) has just one solution modulo d'. Let it be $y + d't$. This yields $\dfrac{m'}{d'}$ incongruent values of y modulo m', each of which, when put in (2), enables us by Theorem 14 to find d' incongruent values of x modulo m'. Then in all we have

$$\frac{m'}{d'} \cdot d' = m' \text{ pairs of values of } x \text{ and } y, \text{ incongruent modulo } m',$$

which satisfy (2).

Let (x_1, y_1) be one such solution of (2). Then $x_1 + m't$ and $y_1 + m't$, where $t = 0, 1, 2, \cdots, d - 1$, represent d values of x and d values of y, which may be paired to give d^2 incongruent solutions, modulo m, of (1). But there are m' pairs of values such as (x_1, y_1). Hence in all we have $d^2m' = dm$ incongruent solutions of (1).

Example. Find the solutions of

(1) $$12x + 10y - 6 \equiv 0 \pmod{42}$$

Here $(12, 10, 42) = 2$, which divides 6. Then we get

(2) $$6x + 5y - 3 \equiv 0 \pmod{21}$$

in which $(6, 21) = 3$. Hence

(3) $$5y - 3 \equiv 0 \pmod 3$$

The solutions of (3), incongruent modulo 21, are $y \equiv 0, 3, 6, 9, 12, 15, 18$. For each of these seven values of y substituted in (2) there are three values of x modulo 21. Thus we get the 21 solutions of (2):

$(4, 0)$, $(5, 3)$, $(6, 6)$, $(0, 9)$, $(1, 12)$, $(2, 15)$, $(3, 18)$,
$(11, 0)$, $(12, 3)$, $(13, 6)$, $(7, 9)$, $(8, 12)$, $(9, 15)$, $(10, 18)$,
$(18, 0)$, $(19, 3)$, $(20, 6)$, $(14, 9)$, $(15, 12)$, $(16, 15)$, $(17, 18)$

But each of these solutions (x, y), when taken in reference to modulus 42, may be written in the form $x + 21t$, $y + 21t$, where $t = 0$ or 1, and therefore will yield four solutions of (1), viz.

$$(x, y), \quad (x + 21, y), \quad (x, y + 21), \quad \text{and} \quad (x + 21, y + 21)$$

For example the solution $(5, 3)$ of (2) yields the solutions $(5, 3)$, $(26, 3)$, $(5, 24)$, and $(26, 24)$ of (1).

Thus a complete tabulation of the roots of (1) would have 84 pairs of values of x and y incongruent modulo 42.

EXERCISES IV

1. Find the number of solutions of $12x - 39y + 3 \equiv 0$ (mod 30). Tabulate the solutions of the reduced congruence (2). Find all solutions of the given congruence which are derived from one solution of the reduced congruence.

2. Find all solutions of the congruence $10x + 7y + 19 \equiv 0$ (mod 15).

3. How many solutions has each of the congruences:

(a) $14x - 7y + 10 \equiv 0$ (mod 28).

(b) $13x + 26y + 39 \equiv 0$ (mod 52).

4. Prove, by induction, that the linear congruence in n unknowns

$$a_1x_1 + a_2x_2 + \cdots + a_nx_n + a_{n+1} \equiv 0 \text{ (mod } m)$$

is satisfied by just dm^{n-1} sets of values incongruent modulo m, where $d = (a_1, a_2, \cdots, a_n, m)$, or has no roots, according as a_{n+1} is, or is not, divisible by d.

Suggestion: Write the reduced congruence

$$(2) \qquad a_1'x_1 + a_2'x_2 + \cdots + a_n'x_n + a_{n+1}' \equiv 0 \text{ (mod } m')$$

Let $(a_1', m') = d'$. Then

$$(3) \qquad a_2'x_2 + a_3'x_3 + \cdots + a_n'x_n + a_{n+1}' \equiv 0 \text{ (mod } d').$$

Assume the theorem true for $n - 1$ unknowns, and enumerate the solutions of (3), then of (2), and finally of (1).

29. Simultaneous congruences.

We now consider the finding of solutions, if any exist, of the *set of simultaneous congruences:*

(1) $x \equiv b_1 \pmod{m_1}$, (2) $x \equiv b_2 \pmod{m_2}$, $\cdots$, (k) $x \equiv b_k \pmod{m_k}$.

From (1), $x = m_1 y + b_1$. Put this value in (2) and $m_1 y + b_1 \equiv b_2$ (mod m_2), or

$$(k + 1) \qquad m_1 y \equiv b_2 - b_1 \text{ (mod } m_2)$$

Now $(k + 1)$, and consequently the pair (1) and (2), is solvable if, and only if, $b_2 - b_1 \equiv 0$ (mod d), where $d = (m_1, m_2)$. Then, if $(k + 1)$ has one or more solutions, they will differ by multiples of $\dfrac{m_2}{d}$, having the form $y_1 + \dfrac{m_2}{d} t$. Hence

$$x = m_1\left(y_1 + \frac{m_2}{d} t\right) + b_1 = m_1 y_1 + b_1 + \frac{m_1 m_2}{d} t$$

Thus the values of x, which satisfy both (1) and (2), differ by multiples of $\dfrac{m_1 m_2}{d}$, which is the l.c.m. of m_1 and m_2. Then, if x_1

is such a value of x, the congruences (1) and (2) may be replaced by the single congruence

$$(k + 2) \qquad x \equiv x_1 \pmod{l_1}$$

where $l_1 = \dfrac{m_1 m_2}{d}$.

Now $(k + 2)$ and (3) may be considered simultaneously, as were (1) and (2), and, if they are solvable, we arrive at a congruence

$$(k + 3) \qquad x \equiv x_2 \pmod{l_2}$$

whose solutions satisfy $(k + 2)$ and (3), and consequently (1), (2), and (3). l_2 is the l.c.m. of l_1 and m_3 and therefore of m_1, m_2, and m_3.

By continuing this process any existing solutions of the set of simultaneous congruences may be found. Such solutions will differ by multiples of the l.c.m. of the moduli. Emphasis should be given to the above necessary and sufficient condition that any two of the congruences have a common solution. We then may state:

THEOREM 16 (*Chinese remainder theorem*). *Numbers which satisfy the congruences* $x \equiv b_1$ (*mod* m_1), $\cdots$, $x \equiv b_k$ (*mod* m_k) *exist if the* m_i *are relatively prime in pairs, and such numbers constitute a single number class modulo* $\overset{k}{\underset{1}{\Pi}} m_i$.

In addition we do not lose sight of the fact that the congruences may have simultaneous solutions even though some or all of the m_i have common factors other than unity.

COROLLARY. *Any number of congruences in one variable and of any degree, such that each has at least one solution, and in which the moduli are relatively prime in pairs, have at least one common solution modulo* l, *the product of the moduli.*

For, let x_1, x_2, $\cdots$, x_k respectively be the roots of k such congruences. By Theorem 16 we can always find a number which is congruent to each x_i with respect to its modulus.

The method of simultaneous congruences can be used in *solving linear congruences with composite moduli*. It is sufficient to illustrate.

Solve

$$(1) \qquad 17x \equiv 2 \pmod{210}.$$

$210 = 2 \cdot 3 \cdot 5 \cdot 7$. Then (1) is equivalent to the set of congruences

$$17x \equiv 2 \pmod{2} \qquad 17x \equiv 2 \pmod{5}$$

$$17x \equiv 2 \pmod{3} \qquad 17x \equiv 2 \pmod{7}$$

Solving each of these, we get respectively

(2) $x \equiv 2 \pmod 2$ (4) $x \equiv 1 \pmod 5$

(3) $x \equiv 1 \pmod 3$ (5) $x \equiv 3 \pmod 7$

From (2) $x = 2y_1 + 2$. Putting this in (3), we get $y_1 = 1 + 3t$ and $x = 4 + 6t$. Hence (2) and (3) are equivalent to

(6) $$x \equiv 4 \pmod 6$$

Combining (6) and (4) we find them to be equivalent to

(7) $$x \equiv 16 \pmod{30}$$

In the same way (7) and (5) may be replaced by

(8) $$x \equiv 136 \pmod{210}$$

which gives the solution of (1).

EXERCISES V

Find a common solution, when such exists, for the sets of congruences:

1. $x \equiv 8 \pmod{15}$, $x \equiv 11 \pmod{21}$,
     $x \equiv 5 \pmod 9$, $x \equiv 2 \pmod{12}$.

2. $x \equiv 9 \pmod{14}$, $x \equiv 6 \pmod{28}$,
     $x \equiv 11 \pmod{20}$.

3. $x^3 \equiv 1 \pmod 7$, $x^2 \equiv 3 \pmod{13}$.

4. $x^{16} \equiv 1 \pmod{17}$, $x^2 \equiv 6 \pmod{11}$.

5. $7x \equiv 5 \pmod{16}$, $x^2 \equiv 5 \pmod{11}$,
     $5x \equiv 6 \pmod{12}$.

6. $x \equiv a \pmod{16}$, $x \equiv b \pmod 5$,
     $x \equiv c \pmod{11}$.

7. Find the two least positive integers having the remainders 2, 3, and 2 when divided by 3, 5, and 7, respectively.

Solve the following congruences by the method of this section:

8. $23x \equiv 77 \pmod{180}$.

9. $13x \equiv 141 \pmod{385}$.

30. Congruences of higher degree. We now consider the general congruence in one unknown

$$f(x) = a_0x^n + a_1x^{n-1} + \cdots + a_n \equiv 0 \pmod m$$

where the a_i are not all congruent to zero modulo m.

We first show how to reduce the general case to that in which the modulus is a power of a prime.

THEOREM 17. *The number of roots of the congruence*

(1) $$f(x) \equiv 0 \ (\mathrm{mod}\ m)$$

is the product of the numbers of roots of the congruences

(2) $$f(x) \equiv 0 \ (\mathrm{mod}\ m_1),\ \cdots, f(x) \equiv 0 \ (\mathrm{mod}\ m_k)$$

where $m = \overset{k}{\underset{1}{\Pi}} m_i$, *and the* m_i *are relatively prime in pairs.*

For by applying Theorem 16 each set of roots of (2) yields one and only one root of (1). Also any number which satisfies (1) obviously satisfies each congruence of (2) uniquely. Thus there is a one-to-one correspondence between the roots of (1) and the sets of roots of (2). Since the number of sets of roots of (2) is the product of the numbers of roots of the individual congruences of (2), the theorem follows.

This theorem is illustrated in solving the congruence

(1') $$x^2 - 9 \equiv 0 \ (\mathrm{mod}\ 91)$$

Factoring the modulus, we form the congruences

(2') $$x^2 - 9 \equiv 0 \ (\mathrm{mod}\ 7)$$

(3') $$x^2 - 9 \equiv 0 \ (\mathrm{mod}\ 13)$$

The roots of (2') are $x \equiv \pm 3$. $x \equiv \pm 3$ are also the roots of (3'). (See Theorem 18 below.) Then the sets of roots of (2') and (3') are $3, 3; 3, -3; -3, 3;$ and $-3, -3$. It appears at once that both 3 and -3 are solutions of (2') and (3') and hence of (1'). The other two solutions of (1') are found by getting the solutions of the two sets of simultaneous congruences

$$x \equiv 3 \ (\mathrm{mod}\ 7) \qquad\qquad x \equiv -3 \ (\mathrm{mod}\ 7)$$

$$x \equiv -3 \ (\mathrm{mod}\ 13) \qquad\qquad x \equiv 3 \ (\mathrm{mod}\ 13)$$

by Theorem 16. These solutions are 10 and -10, respectively. Hence the four solutions of (1') are $\pm 3, \pm 10$.

Now if in (1) $m = \Pi p_i^{\alpha_i}$ is the factorization of m into powers of distinct primes, we have merely to set $m = \Pi p_i^{\alpha_i}$ in order to obtain the desired reduction.

Now the m_i of the general congruence (1) may be taken as powers of distinct primes, and thus the study of congruences is reduced to the study of those having powers of primes as moduli.

31. Factor theorem modulo p. We then consider first the congruence

$$(3) \qquad f(x) = a_0x^n + a_1x^{n-1} + \cdots + a_n \equiv 0 \pmod{p}$$

in which the modulus is a prime.

We shall sometimes find it necessary to regard x in $f(x)$ not as a number but as a mere indeterminate symbol. If x is such an indeterminate, a congruence like

$$f(x) \equiv g(x) = b_0x^n + b_1x^{n-1} + \cdots + b_n \pmod{p}$$

is to be interpreted as meaning

$$a_0 \equiv b_0, a_1 \equiv b_1, \cdots, a_n \equiv b_n \pmod{p}$$

or, if we prefer, that
$$f(x) = g(x) + p \cdot h(x)$$

$h(x)$ being a polynomial with *integral* coefficients, is an algebraic identity. We shall speak of this relation as *identical congruence* of $f(x)$ and $g(x)$.

If $f(x) \equiv g(x) \pmod{p}$ identically, then by Theorem 3 $f(a) \equiv g(a)$, where a is any integer. But $f(a) \equiv g(a)$ for all integers does not imply $f(x) \equiv g(x)$ identically. For example, $a^5 \equiv 6a \pmod{5}$ for all integral values of a, but $x^5 \equiv 6x \pmod{5}$ is not an identical congruence. This is in contrast to the case of algebraic identity of polynomials.

Algebraic division of two polynomials $f(x)$ by $g(x)$ leads to an algebraic identity of the form

$$f(x) = q(x) \cdot g(x) + r(x)$$

Here if the degree of $g(x)$ is m, then the degree of $q(x)$ is $n - m$, while that of $r(x)$ does not exceed $m - 1$. If the coefficients in $f(x)$ and $g(x)$ are all integers and the leading coefficient of $g(x)$ is unity, the coefficients in $q(x)$ and $r(x)$ will all be integers. If in the process of performing the division we alter any of the coefficients by adding or subtracting multiples of p, we are led to an identical congruence

$$f(x) \equiv q(x) \cdot g(x) + r(x) \pmod{p}$$

Such division is called *division modulo p*. If $r(x) \equiv 0 \pmod{p}$, $g(x)$ is said to be a *factor modulo p* of $f(x)$.

A polynomial of the highest degree which is a factor modulo p of each of two polynomials is said to be their *g.c.d. modulo p*.   It can be found by the Euclidean algorithm for finding the g.c.d. This is seen in algebra to be applicable to ordinary polynomials. It is also applicable to polynomials modulo p, provided that the divisions are performed modulo p.

In particular, if for $g(x)$ we take $x - a$, $r(x)$ will be a constant, and we have the identical congruence

$$f(x) \equiv q(x) \cdot (x - a) + r \pmod{p}$$

The necessary and sufficient condition for a to be a root of (3) is that $r \equiv 0 \pmod{p}$, for then

$$f(a) \equiv q(a) \cdot (a - a) \equiv 0 \pmod{p}$$

Thus, if a *is a root of* $f(x) \equiv 0$ *(mod* p*),* $(x - a)$ *is a factor modulo* p *of* $f(x)$.

For example, we see that 2 is a root of

(4) $$6x^3 + 5x^2 + 5x - 1 \equiv 0 \pmod{7}$$

By division modulo 7

$$6x^3 + 5x^2 + 5x - 1 \equiv (6x^2 + 3x + 4)(x - 2) \pmod{7}$$

and $x - 2$ is a factor modulo 7 of the left member.   Now since 7 is a prime any other roots of (4) must satisfy

$$6x^2 + 3x + 4 \equiv 0 \pmod{7}$$

Evidently

$$6x^2 + 3x + 4 \equiv -x^2 + 3x + 4 = (x + 1)(-x + 4) \pmod{7}$$

which shows -1 and 4 to be roots of this congruence and hence of (4).

As an example of a congruence having no root we write

$$x^2 - 8x + 13 \equiv 0 \pmod{5}$$

There are but five integers modulo 5 to consider as possible roots, and by actual substitution in the given congruence or in $x^2 + 2x - 2 \equiv 0$ these may be seen not to satisfy the congruence.

32. Number of roots.   Theorem 18, now to be proved, is entirely analogous to the corresponding theorem for algebraic equations if only real roots of the latter are considered. Indeed we recall that if the n roots of the algebraic equation

$$(5) \qquad f(x) = a_0 x^n + a_1 x^{n-1} + \cdots + a_n = 0$$

are $\alpha_1, \alpha_2, \cdots, \alpha_n$, then

$$(6) \qquad f(x) = a_0(x - \alpha_1)(x - \alpha_2) \cdots (x - \alpha_n)$$

It will be further recalled that by comparing coefficients of like powers of x in (5) and (6) we find that $a_i = (-1)^i a_0$ times the sum of the products of the roots taken i at a time. This result will be found presently to have an analogue for congruences.

THEOREM 18. *A congruence of degree* n, *in one unknown with a prime modulus, whose coefficients are not all zero, has at most* n *distinct roots.*

To prove this we assume that (3) has the n roots $\alpha_1, \alpha_2, \alpha_3, \cdots, \alpha_n$. Then by the above discussion $f(x) \equiv q_{n-1}(x)(x - \alpha_1)$ (mod p), in which $q_{n-1}(x)$ denotes a polynomial in x of degree $n - 1$. In the same way, since α_2 is a root of $q_{n-1}(x) \equiv 0$ (mod p), we have

$$q_{n-1}(x) \equiv q_{n-2}(x)(x - \alpha_2) \text{ (mod } p)$$

or $\qquad f(x) \equiv q_{n-2}(x)(x - \alpha_2)(x - \alpha_1) \text{ (mod } p)$

And finally,

$$(7) \qquad f(x) \equiv a_0(x - \alpha_n)(x - \alpha_{n-1}) \cdots (x - \alpha_1) \text{ (mod } p)$$

Now if (3) has a root β distinct from the α_i, then

$$(8) \qquad f(\beta) \equiv a_0(\beta - \alpha_n)(\beta - \alpha_{n-1}) \cdots (\beta - \alpha_1) \text{ (mod } p)$$

and, since $a_0 \not\equiv 0$, one of the factors $\beta - \alpha_i \equiv 0$, which contradicts the assumption that β is distinct from the α_i. Hence the theorem.

COROLLARY 1. *If* (3) *has the* n *distinct roots* $\alpha_1, \alpha_2, \cdots, \alpha_n$, *then* $a_i \equiv (-1)^i a_0$ *times the sum of the product of the* α's *taken* i *at a time (mod* p).

This follows by comparing coefficients in the identical congruence (7).

It is clear that the discussion of the theorem is not changed if two or more of the roots are equal.

Suppose that (3) has $n + 1$ distinct roots. From (8) this requires that $a_0 \equiv 0$. The congruence is then of at most degree

$n - 1$. And by the same argument, a_1, and finally all the a_i, would be $\equiv 0$. Hence:

COROLLARY 2. *If a congruence of degree* n *in one unknown, and with a prime modulus, has* n $+ 1$ *distinct roots, then its coefficients are all divisible by the modulus.*

When p is a prime, it follows from Fermat's theorem that the congruence $x^{p-1} - 1 \equiv 0 \pmod{p}$ has the roots $1, 2, 3, \cdots, p - 1$. Therefore we have

$$x^{p-1} - 1 \equiv (x - 1)(x - 2) \cdots (x - p + 1) \pmod{p}$$

or $x^{p-1} - 1 - (x - 1)(x - 2) \cdots (x - p + 1) \equiv 0 \pmod{p}$

In this congruence, which has $p - 1$ distinct roots, the coefficient of x^{p-1} is zero. Hence by Corollary 2 all coefficients of the congruence are divisible by p, and by Corollary 1 we have

THEOREM 19. *If* p *is a prime and* r *is any number less than* p $- 1$, *the sum of the products of the numbers* $1, 2, 3, \cdots,$ p $- 1$ *taken* r *at a time is divisible by* p.

Also we have here a second proof of Wilson's theorem, since from the constant term of the congruence $(p - 1)! + 1$ is divisible by p.

We can now prove

THEOREM 20. *If* p *is a prime and* d *is a divisor of* p $- 1$, *there are exactly* d *roots of the congruence*

(1) $$x^d - 1 \equiv 0 \pmod{p}$$

Since d is a divisor of $p - 1$, we have by algebraic factorization

$$x^{p-1} - 1 \equiv (x^d - 1) \cdot q(x) \pmod{p}$$

where $q(x)$ is a polynomial of degree $p - 1 - d$ in x, not all of whose coefficients are zero. Then the congruence

$$q(x) \equiv 0 \pmod{p}$$

has *at most* $p - 1 - d$ roots. And since the congruence

$$x^{p-1} - 1 \equiv 0 \pmod{p}$$

has *exactly* $p-1$ roots, (1) must have *at least* $p-1-(p-1-d)=d$ roots. But, by Theorem 18, (1) has at most d roots. Hence it has just d roots.

The following is of theoretical interest in finding the roots of a congruence, and illustrates division with respect to a modulus. Let it be desired to find the roots of   (1) $f(x) \equiv 0 \pmod{p}$, of degree $n \leqq p - 1$, p an odd prime, and of which zero is not a root.

The congruence   (2) $x^{p-1} - 1 \equiv 0 \pmod{p}$, we know, has just $p - 1$ roots.   Let $g(x)$ of degree $r \leqq n$ be the g.c.d. modulo p of $f(x)$ and $x^{p-1} - 1$.   Then the congruence   (3) $g(x) \equiv 0 \pmod{p}$ has just r distinct roots, for (2) has $p - 1$ roots and $g(x)$ is a factor of $x^{p-1} - 1$.   These r roots of (3) are also roots of (1).   Moreover, any root of (1), since it is also a root of (2), must be a root of (3). Hence we see that (1) has just r distinct roots, and they are the roots of (3).   However, some of these roots may be multiple roots of (1), though (3) cannot have multiple roots because (2) has none.

To illustrate, find the roots of

(1) $2x^4 + x^3 - 2x^2 - 3x + 2 \equiv 0 \pmod{7}$

The g.c.d. modulo 7 of this polynomial and $x^6 - 1$ is $5x^2 - x + 3$. Then the roots of

(2) $5x^2 - x + 3 \equiv 0 \pmod{7}$

are found to be 1 and 2.   Hence they are the distinct roots of (1).

Dividing $2x^4 + x^3 - 2x^2 - 3x + 2$ by $(x - 1)(x - 2)$, or by $5x^2 - x + 3 \equiv -2(x - 1)(x - 2)$, the quotient is congruent to $x^2 + 4$, and neither $x \equiv 1$, or 2 is a root of $x^2 + 4 \equiv 0 \pmod{7}$. Therefore $x \equiv 1, 2$ are the only roots of (1).

EXERCISES VI

Find all the solutions of the congruences:

1. $x^2 - 2 \equiv 0 \pmod{161}$.

2. $x^2 - 3 \equiv 0 \pmod{143}$.

3. $x^2 - 5 \equiv 0 \pmod{77}$.

4. Determine the number of solutions of the congruence $x^6 - 1 \equiv 0 \pmod{35}$.

5. Show that the g.c.d. of $x^4 - 4x^3 - x^2 - 2x - 2$ and $x^4 - 1$ modulo 5 is a constant, and hence that the congruence $x^4 - 4x^3 - x^2 - 2x - 2 \equiv 0 \pmod{5}$ has no solution.

6. Find the roots of $4x^3 - 8x^2 - 3x + 3 \equiv 0 \pmod{11}$.

33. Power residues.   The powers of a, or the number classes defined by them, modulo m are known as *power residues of a modulo* m.   For example, the powers of 2: 2, 4, 8, 16, 32, 64, 128, 256, $\cdots$ when taken modulo 9 are congruent respectively to 2, 4, 8, 7, 5, 1, 2, 4, $\cdots$, the latter being referred to as the power residues of 2 modulo 9. Likewise the power residues of 5 modulo 12 are 5, 1, 5, 1, ⋯.

In general we will assume $(a, m) = 1$. Then the powers of a are prime to m and, when reduced to their least positive values modulo m, must be less than m and prime to it. Since there are but $\phi(m)$ such values, if more than $\phi(m)$ powers of a are taken, at least two of them must be congruent. Let $a^s \equiv a^r \pmod{m}$, $s > r$. Then $a^{s-r} \equiv 1 \pmod{m}$.

If t is the *least* positive exponent for which $a^t \equiv 1 \pmod{m}$, then *a is said to belong to the exponent* t *modulo* m. This relationship may be indicated symbolically thus, $a \to t(m)$, or if the modulus does not need to be specified, simply $a \to t$. In the above examples it appears that $2 \to 6(9)$ and $5 \to 2(12)$.

THEOREM 21. *If* a $\to$ t(m), *and if* $a^u \equiv 1$ (*mod* m), *then* u *is a multiple of* t.

For let $u = qt + r$, where $0 \leq r < t$. Then $a^u = a^{qt+r} = a^{qt} \cdot a^r \equiv a^r \pmod{m}$. But since $a^u \equiv 1$ we get $a^r \equiv 1$, and this contradicts the hypothesis that t is the least exponent for which $a^t \equiv 1$, unless $r = 0$. Hence $u = qt$.

We recall now that $a^{\phi(m)} \equiv 1 \pmod{m}$, and therefore can state the

COROLLARY. *If* a $\to$ t(m), *then* t *is a divisor of* ϕ(m).

The following is a complete table of power residues modulo 13. The top row shows the indices of the powers. The third row contains the residues of the powers of 2; the fourth row, the same for 3, etc. Illustrations of the above theorem and corollary may be easily noted. The least numerical residues are used.

POWER RESIDUES MODULO 13

i	a 1	2	3	4	5	6	7	8	9	10	11	12
1	1	1	1	1	1	1	1	1	1	1	1	1
2	2	4	-5	3	6	-1	-2	-4	5	-3	-6	1
3	3	-4	1	3	-4	1	3	-4	1	3	-4	1
4	4	3	-1	-4	-3	1	4	3	-1	-4	-3	1
5	5	-1	-5	1	5	-1	-5	1	5	-1	-5	1
6	6	-3	-5	-4	2	-1	-6	3	5	4	-2	1
-6	-6	-3	5	-4	-2	-1	6	3	-5	4	2	1
-5	-5	-1	5	1	-5	-1	5	1	-5	-1	5	1
-4	-4	3	1	-4	3	1	-4	3	1	-4	3	1
-3	-3	-4	-1	3	4	1	-3	-4	-1	3	4	1
-2	-2	4	5	3	-6	-1	2	-4	-5	-3	6	1
-1	-1	1	-1	1	-1	1	-1	1	-1	1	-1	1

EXERCISES VII

1. Make a complete table of power residues for modulus 19.
2. Do the same for modulus 10.
3. Do the same for modulus 29.

THEOREM 22.   *If* a $\rightarrow$ t *and* b $\rightarrow$ u *modulo* m, *where* (t, u) = 1, *then* ab $\rightarrow$ tu(m).

To prove this, assume $(ab)^w \equiv 1 \pmod{m}$. Then $1 \equiv (ab)^w \equiv (ab)^{wt} \equiv a^{wt}b^{wt} \equiv b^{wt}$. Hence, by Theorem 21, wt, and consequently w, is a multiple of u. In a similar way we find that w is a multiple of t also, or, since $(t, u) = 1$, w is a multiple of tu. Now $(ab)^{tu} \equiv a^{tu}b^{tu} \equiv 1$. Hence tu itself is the least value of w for which $(ab)^w \equiv 1 \pmod{m}$. Therefore $ab \rightarrow tu$.

In preparation for the next theorem we prove the

LEMMA.   *If one number* a *belongs to the exponent* t *modulo* p, *a prime, then* ϕ(t) *numbers belong to* t *modulo* p.

All numbers which belong to t are roots of the congruence (1) $x^t \equiv 1 \pmod{p}$. By the Corollary to Theorem 21, t is a divisor of $p - 1$, and hence by Theorem 20 there are just t roots of this congruence.

By hypothesis $a \rightarrow t$. The numbers $a, a^2, a^3, \cdots, a^t$, all of which satisfy (1), are incongruent modulo p. For if $a^s \equiv a^r \pmod{p}$, where $0 < r < s < t$, then $a^{s-r} \equiv 1 \pmod{p}$, where $s - r < t$, which is impossible. Therefore these t powers of a include all possible numbers which may belong to t modulo p.

We now determine the values of i for which $a^i \rightarrow t$. Assume $a^i \rightarrow r$. Then $(a^i)^r = a^{ir} \equiv 1$. But $(a^i)^t \equiv 1$. Hence $r \leqq t$. By Theorem 21 ir is divisible by t.

First we assume $(i, t) = 1$, in which case r is divisible by t. Hence $r = t$.

But if $(i, t) = \delta > 1$, with $i = i'\delta$, $t = t'\delta$, then

$$(a^i)^{t'} = a^{i'\delta t'} = (a^{i'})^t \equiv 1$$

Hence $r \leqq t' < t$, and a^i belongs to an exponent $<t$.

Then, since r, the exponent to which a^i belongs, $=t$ when $(i, t) = 1$ and $<t$ when $(i, t) = \delta > 1$, it follows that $a^i \rightarrow t$ when and only when $(i, t) = 1$. Hence the lemma.

THEOREM 23.   *If* t *is a divisor of* p $-$ 1, *there are* ϕ(t) *incongruent numbers modulo* p *which belong to* t *as an exponent,*

Let t_i represent the divisors of $p - 1$ as i takes the values 1, 2, $\cdots$, $\nu(p - 1)$.

Let $\psi(t_i)$ be the number of integers 1, 2, 3, $\cdots$, $(p - 1)$ which belong to t_i. By the above lemma $\psi(t_i) =$ either $\phi(t_i)$ or 0.

By the Corollary to Theorem 21 each of the integers 1, 2, $\cdots$, $p - 1$ belongs to some one of the t_i. Hence

$$\Sigma \psi(t_i) = p - 1$$

But we also know by Exercise 4, page 13, that

$$\Sigma \phi(t_i) = p - 1$$

Therefore $$\Sigma \psi(t_i) = \Sigma \phi(t_i)$$

which is possible only when $\psi(t_i) = \phi(t_i)$ for all values of i. Hence the theorem.

34. Primitive roots. If the number to which a belongs modulo m is $\phi(m)$, then a is called a *primitive root* of m. In particular, by the theorem just proved a prime p has $\phi(p - 1)$ primitive roots.

For example, from the above table for modulus 13, the primitive roots of 13 are seen to be 2, 6, -6, -2. There are $\phi(12) = 4$ of them.

EXERCISES VIII

1. Find illustrations of Theorems 21, 22, and 23 in the table of power residues for the modulus 13.

2. Do the same for modulus 19.

3. Do the same for modulus 29.

4. Illustrate the lemma preceding Theorem 23 from one of the tables of power residues.

Then solve the problem: Given that $15 \rightarrow 10(31)$, find all values of x such that $x \rightarrow 10(31)$.

5. Given that $30 \rightarrow 2$, $5 \rightarrow 3$, and $2 \rightarrow 5$ modulo 31, find numbers belonging respectively to the exponents 6, 10, 15, and 30. Find all the primitive roots of 31.

6. Determine a primitive root of 109.

7. Prove that the numbers which belong to any given exponent $t > 2$ modulo $p > 3$ occur in pairs such that the product of the numbers of a pair is congruent to 1 modulo p.

8. Prove that if $a \rightarrow t(p)$, then $a^k \equiv a^l \pmod{p}$, if and only if $k - l \equiv 0 \pmod{t}$.

9. Find the exponents to which 10 belongs modulo 7, modulo 23, and modulo 27. Change $\frac{1}{7}$, $\frac{3}{7}$, $\frac{1}{23}$, $\frac{6}{23}$, $\frac{1}{27}$ to circulating decimals.

10. Prove that if p is a prime distinct from 2 and 5, and if $0 < a < p$, the fraction $\dfrac{a}{p}$ can be expressed as a pure circulating decimal, and the number of digits in the period is the exponent to which 10 belongs modulo p.

11. Prove that if l is the *least* exponent for which for some value of k $a^l \equiv b^k \pmod{m}$, where a and b are each prime to m, then whenever $a^n \equiv b^j$ $\pmod{m}$ it follows that $n \equiv 0 \pmod{l}$. Find an illustration of this proposition in one of the tables of power residues.

12. Prove that if $a \equiv b \pmod{p^k}$, where a and b are each prime to p, then $a^{p^s} \equiv b^{p^s} \pmod{p^{k+s}}$. *Suggestion:* Change the congruence to an equation, raise to the pth power by the binomial theorem, and use induction on s. This proposition will be useful in some of the discussions to follow.

13. Show that, if $a \to t(p)$, then $a^u \to \dfrac{t}{d}\,(p)$, where $d = (u, t)$ and p is a prime.

14. Show that, if $a \to \dfrac{p-1}{2}\,(p)$, where p is a prime of the form $4n - 1$, then $-a$ is a primitive root of p.

How can this be used in part of the computation of Exercise 5 above?

15. Show that $p - 1$ occurs as a power residue of b modulo p if, and only if, the exponent to which b belongs is even.

16. If $a \to t(p)$, show that the product of a complete set of power residues of a is congruent to -1 or 1 modulo p, according as t is even or odd.

17. Show that the proposition of Exercise 16 affords another proof of Wilson's theorem.

35. Numbers having primitive roots.

From Theorem 23 it follows that a prime p has $\phi(p - 1)$ primitive roots. We will now determine which of the composite integers have primitive roots.

Let $m = \overset{k}{\underset{1}{\Pi}}\, m_i$, in which the m_i are powers of distinct primes, and assume that there are as many as two of the m_i greater than 2. Now $\phi(m) = \overset{k}{\underset{1}{\Pi}}\, \phi(m_i)$, in which each $\phi(m_i)$ for $m_i > 2$ is even. Hence the l.c.m. of the $\phi(m_i)$ is $M < \phi(m)$.

Now let a be any integer prime to m, whence $a^M \equiv 1 \pmod{m_i}$ for all values of i. Hence $a^M \equiv 1 \pmod{m}$. And since $M < \phi(m)$ it follows that m has no primitive root.

Examples of integers which therefore do not have primitive roots are $15 = 3 \cdot 5$, $30 = 2 \cdot 3 \cdot 5$, $12 = 4 \cdot 3$, and $45 = 3^2 \cdot 5$.

The forms of integers remaining to be considered are 2^n, p^n, and $2p^n$, where p is an odd prime.

First we examine 2^n. This has primitive roots for $n = 1$ and $n = 2$, since 1 may be considered a primitive root of 2, and 3 is a primitive root of 4. But we find by the following argument that for $n > 2$, 2^n has no primitive roots.

Any possible primitive root a of 2^n must be odd. Then $a^2 = 1 + 8b \equiv 1 \pmod{2^3}$. (See Exercise 6, page 3.) Applying Exercise 12 above, we have $(a^2)^{2^{n-3}} = a^{2^{n-2}} \equiv 1 \pmod{2^n}$. But $2^{n-2} < 2^{n-1} = \phi(2^n)$. *Hence 2^n, for n > 2, has no primitive root.*

We will now show that *integers of the form* p^n, p *an odd prime, have primitive roots.* Let g be a primitive root of p. Then

(1)
$$(g + pt)^{p-1} \equiv 1 \pmod{p}$$

for all values of t. First we seek a value of t such that

(2)
$$(g + pt)^{p-1} \not\equiv 1 \pmod{p^2}$$

or
$$(g + pt)^p - (g + pt) \not\equiv 0 \pmod{p^2}$$

for unless (2) is satisfied $g + pt$ cannot be a primitive root of p^2.

By the binomial theorem this becomes

$$g^p + p^2 H_1 - g - pt \not\equiv 0 \pmod{p^2}$$

or
$$g^p - g - pt \not\equiv 0 \pmod{p^2}$$

But $g^p - g \equiv 0 \pmod{p}$ or $g^p - g = np$. Hence

$$np - pt = p(n - t) \not\equiv 0 \pmod{p^2}$$

when and only when $n - t \not\equiv 0 \pmod{p}$. That is, we require a value of t satisfying this linear incongruence. Clearly there are $p - 1$ such.

We assume any such value of t, put $g + pt = r$, and will show that r is a primitive root of p^n. From (1) and (2) $r^{p-1} \equiv 1 \pmod{p}$ and $r^{p-1} \not\equiv 1 \pmod{p^2}$. Hence

(3)
$$r^{p-1} = 1 + kp, \quad \text{where} \quad k \not\equiv 0 \pmod{p}$$

Now, since by the binomial theorem

$$(1 + kp)^p = 1 + kp^2 + H_2 p^3$$

we have

(4)
$$(1 + kp)^p \equiv 1 + kp^2 \pmod{p^3}$$

Applying the proposition of Exercise 12 above to (4) with $s = n-3$, $n > 2$, we get

(5)
$$(1 + kp)^{p^{n-2}} \equiv (1 + kp^2)^{p^{n-3}} \pmod{p^n}$$

By the binomial theorem again we have

$$(1 + kp^2)^{p^{n-3}} = 1 + kp^{n-1} + H_3 p^{n+1} \equiv 1 + kp^{n-1} \pmod{p^n}$$

Using this in (5)

$$(1 + kp)^{p^{n-2}} \equiv 1 + kp^{n-1} \pmod{p^n}$$

By (3) this becomes

$$r^{(p-1)p^{n-2}} \equiv 1 + kp^{n-1} \pmod{p^n}$$

Since $k \not\equiv 0 \pmod{p}$, we have

(6) $$r^{(p-1)p^{n-2}} \not\equiv 1 \pmod{p^n}$$

which by (2) is also true for $n = 2$.

Now let $r \to e(p^n)$. Then e is a divisor of $\phi(p^n) = p^{n-1}(p - 1)$. But, since $r^e \equiv 1 \pmod{p^n}$, then also $r^e \equiv 1 \pmod{p}$, and e is a multiple of $p - 1$. Hence e is of the form $p^u(p - 1)$. From (6) it appears that $u > n - 2$. Also $u \leq n - 1$. Hence $u = n - 1$, $e = p^{n-1}(p - 1)$, and $r = g + pt$ is a primitive root of p^n.

Integers of the form $2p^n$ remain to be considered. Let g be a primitive root of p^n, and assume first that g is odd. Then $g^e - 1$ is divisible alike by p^n and $2p^n$. Also $\phi(2p^n) = \phi(p^n)$. Hence g is a primitive root of $2p^n$. If g is even we replace it by $g + p^n$ which is odd and by the same argument $g + p^n$ is a primitive root of $2p^n$.

The results of our discussion of numbers which have primitive roots are stated in

THEOREM 24. *An integer* m *has primitive roots if and only if it is* 2, 4, p^n, *or* $2p^n$, *where* p *is an odd prime. If* g *is a primitive root of* p, *and* $(g + tp)^{p-1} \not\equiv 1 \pmod{p^2}$, *then* g + tp *is a primitive root of* p^n.

EXERCISES IX

1. Show that the condition $g^{p-1} \not\equiv 1 \pmod{p^2}$ is necessary for g, a primitive root of p, to be also a primitive root of p^n.

Suggestion: Assume $g^{p-1} \equiv 1 \pmod{p^2}$ and use Exercises VIII, 12, to show that as a consequence g would not be a primitive root of p^n.

2. Show that, if g is a primitive root of p^n, it is also a primitive root of p.

3. Show that there are $(p - 1)\phi(p - 1)$ primitive roots of p^n incongruent modulo p^2.

4. Prove by the use of Exercises 1, 2, and 3 that there are just $\phi[\phi(p^n)]$ primitive roots of p^n.

5. Prove the same result independently by means of powers of one primitive root.

6. Prove that there is the same number of primitive roots of $2p^n$ as of p^n.

7. Find all the primitive roots of 49, expressing them as powers of one of their own number.

8. Do the same for 54.

9. Find a primitive root of 11^5.

36. Indices. We have seen that the powers of a primitive root g of a prime p form a reduced residue system modulo p. Thus any integer c prime to p is associated with a certain index i of the power to which g is raised to produce c, or a number congruent to it, modulo p. That is, $g^i \equiv c \pmod{p}$, and, in a manner analogous to logarithms, i is called the index of c to the base g. This is written $i = \text{ind}_g c$, or $i = \text{ind } c$ when it is unnecessary to indicate the base.

The numbers c are arranged in number classes modulo p but their indices are taken modulo $p - 1$. For if $g^{i_1} \equiv g^{i_2} \pmod{p}$, or $g^{i_1 - i_2} \equiv 1 \pmod{p}$, then $i_1 - i_2 \equiv 0 \pmod{p - 1}$ (Exercises VIII, 8). It is readily shown that the indices obey the laws stated in:

THEOREM 25A. *The index of the product of two numbers is congruent modulo* p − 1 *to the sum of the indices of the numbers.*

For, if $g^{i_1} \equiv c_1$ and $g^{i_2} \equiv c_2$, then

$$g^{i_1} \cdot g^{i_2} = g^{i_1 + i_2} \equiv c_1 \cdot c_2$$

This is readily extended to the product of any number of factors.

THEOREM 25B. *The index of the* n*th power of a number is congruent modulo* p − 1 *to* n *times the index of the number.*

For if $g^i \equiv c$, then $(g^i)^n \equiv g^{ni} \equiv c^n$.

To illustrate from the power residues of 2 modulus 29:

(1) $$27 \cdot 23 \equiv 2^{15} \cdot 2^{20} \equiv 2^{35} \equiv 2^7 \equiv 12 \pmod{29}$$

Using indices the statement may be written thus:

Let $$x \equiv 27 \cdot 23 \pmod{29}$$

$$\text{ind}_2 x \equiv \text{ind}_2 27 + \text{ind}_2 23 \pmod{28}$$

$$\equiv 15 + 20 \equiv 7 \pmod{28}$$

$$\therefore x \equiv 12 \pmod{29}$$

(2) Find
$$x \equiv 10^6 \pmod{29}$$
$$\text{ind } x \equiv 6 \text{ ind } 10 \pmod{28}$$
$$\equiv 6 \cdot 23 \equiv 26 \pmod{28}$$
$$\therefore x \equiv 22 \pmod{29}$$

37. Application to congruences. The indices find ready application in the solution of certain types of congruences when a table is available for the modulus of the congruence.

To solve the *linear congruence*

$$ax \equiv b \pmod{p} \qquad p \text{ a prime}$$

we write $\qquad$ ind $a +$ ind $x \equiv$ ind $b \pmod{p-1}$

or $\qquad\qquad\qquad$ ind $x \equiv$ ind $b -$ ind $a \pmod{p-1}$

and the value of x may be read from the table.

To illustrate, solve

$$18x \equiv 25 \pmod{29}$$
$$\text{ind}_2 18 + \text{ind}_2 x \equiv \text{ind}_2 25 \pmod{28}$$
$$\text{ind}_2 x \equiv 16 - 11 \equiv 5 \pmod{28}$$
$$\therefore x \equiv 3 \pmod{29}$$

We now discuss the solution of the *binomial congruence*.

(1) $\qquad\qquad\qquad x^n \equiv c \pmod{p} \qquad p \text{ a prime}$

By indices we have

(2) $\qquad\qquad\qquad n \text{ ind } x \equiv \text{ ind } c \pmod{p-1}$

which is solvable if and only if $d = (n, p-1)$ divides ind c. This is the condition therefore for the solvability of (1). This condition being satisfied, there are d roots. Hence we conclude that (1) *has the maximum number* n *of roots when and only when* n *divides both* p $-$ 1 *and ind* c (*i.e.,* d $=$ n).

EXERCISES X

Solve the congruences:

1. $x^{10} \equiv 6 \pmod{19}$. $\qquad$ **2.** $x^{10} \equiv 8 \pmod{19}$. $\qquad$ **3.** $x^6 \equiv 11 \pmod{19}$.

4. Make a table of indices for the prime 101 to the base 2.

5. Find two consecutive integers in this table such that their indices differ by 4.

6. Prove that there is one and only one value of x for which ind $(x + 1)$ $-$ ind $x \equiv d$ (mod $p - 1$), where $d \not\equiv 0$ (mod $p - 1$).

By the use of indices solve the congruences:

7. $51x \equiv 88$ (mod 101).   **11.** $x^7 \equiv 48$ (mod 101).

8. $5x^2 \equiv 96$ (mod 101).   **12.** $(x - 3)^4 \equiv 5$ (mod 101).

9. $x^5 \equiv 41$ (mod 101).   **13.** $x^2 + 10x + 5 \equiv 0$ (mod 101).

10. $x^{17} \equiv 75$ (mod 101).

38. The congruence $x^n \equiv c$ (mod p^s). In order to discuss the solutions of the congruence $x^n \equiv c$ (mod p^s), where p is an odd prime which does not divide n or c, we extend the theory of indices to include moduli of the form p^s. Let g be a primitive root of p^s, and consequently of p also. Then the numbers g, g^2, g^3, $\cdots$, g^e, $\cdots$, $g^{p^{s-1}(p-1)}$ form a reduced residue system, modulo p^s. The exponents, or indices, of the system may be arranged in cycles modulo $p - 1$ by putting them in the form $k(p - 1) + i$. In this form i takes the values $1, 2, 3, \cdots, p - 1$ and k successively is $0, 1, 2, \cdots, p^{s-1} - 1$.

Two numbers of the system belong to the same number class modulo p if and only if their indices differ by multiples of $p - 1$. For since g is a primitive root of p, $g^{l_1} \equiv g^{l_2}$ (mod p) if and only if $l_1 \equiv l_2$ (mod $p - 1$). (See Exercise 8, Section 34.)

The solution of the congruence $x^n \equiv c$ (mod p^s) could be effected directly by means of a table of indices modulo p^s, but such is not easily available. The following theorem relating its roots to those of the congruence $x^n \equiv c$ (mod p) is of importance.

THEOREM 26. *The congruences* (1) $x^n \equiv c$ *(mod* p^s*) and* (2) $x^n \equiv c$ *(mod* p*), where* p *is an odd prime that does not divide* n *or* c*, have the same number of solutions; and the solutions of* (1) *are congruent modulo* p *respectively to the solutions of* (2).

First we show the number of solutions to be the same. Put $c \equiv g^{k(p-1)+i}$, and (1) becomes

$$x^n \equiv g^{k(p-1)+i} \pmod{p^s}$$

Then

(3) n ind $x \equiv k(p - 1) + i$ (mod $p^{s-1}(p - 1)$)

Since p does not divide n, the g.c.d. of the modulus of (3) and n is $(p - 1, n) = d$. Therefore (1) has d solutions or none according as d does or does not divide i.

Similarly, putting the value of $c \equiv g^{k(p-1)+i}$ in (2), we have

$$x^n \equiv g^{k(p-1)+i} \equiv g^i \pmod{p}$$

Then $\qquad\qquad n \operatorname{ind} x \equiv i \pmod{p-1}$

from which we see that (2) has just $d = (n, p - 1)$ solutions or none according as d does or does not divide i.

To prove the second part of the theorem we notice first that each solution of (1) is congruent modulo p to a solution of (2). For if $x_1^n - c \equiv 0 \pmod{p^s}$, then $x_1^n - c \equiv 0 \pmod{p}$.

Moreover, no two solutions of (1) can differ by a multiple of p. For let x_1 and x_2 be two solutions of (1), thus implying that $d > 1$. Then putting them in (3) and subtracting results we have

$$n(\operatorname{ind} x_1 - \operatorname{ind} x_2) \equiv 0 \pmod{p^{s-1}(p-1)}$$

Or, since $(n, p) = 1$ and $(n, p - 1) = d$

$$\operatorname{ind} x_1 - \operatorname{ind} x_2 \equiv 0 \left(\bmod p^{s-1} \cdot \frac{p-1}{d}\right)$$

Then the difference between the indices of x_1 and x_2 is divisible by p^{s-1}, but not by $p - 1$. For, if it were divisible also by $p - 1$, we would have

$$\operatorname{ind} x_1 - \operatorname{ind} x_2 \equiv 0 \pmod{p^{s-1}(p-1)}$$

and $\qquad\qquad x_1 - x_2 \equiv 0 \pmod{p^s}$

That is, x_1 and x_2 would not be distinct roots of (1).

Hence, since these indices cannot differ by a multiple of $p - 1$, x_1 and x_2 cannot differ by a multiple of p.

Consequently the correspondence between the roots of (1) and (2) referred to above is one to one.

In terms of number classes, each solution of (1) is a subclass of the corresponding solution of (2).

Example. Find the solutions of (1) $x^2 \equiv 2 \pmod{7^3}$. The solutions of $x^2 \equiv 2 \pmod{7}$ are $x \equiv \pm 3$. Find now solutions of (2) $x^2 \equiv 2 \pmod{7^2}$ by putting $x \equiv 3 + 7t$. Then $9 + 6 \cdot 7t + 7^2 t^2 \equiv 2 \pmod{7^2}$; i.e., $9 - 2 + 6 \cdot 7t \equiv 0 \pmod{7^2}$ or $1 + 6t \equiv 0 \pmod{7}$ and $t \equiv 1$. Then $x \equiv 3 + 7 \equiv 10$ is a solution of (2). Then put $x \equiv 10 + 7^2 t$, and $x \equiv 39 + 7^2 t$ in (1), and by similar method get $x \equiv 108$. If we start with $x = -3 + 7t$, we are led to the second solution $x \equiv -108$.

EXERCISES XI

Find the solutions of the congruences:

1. $x^2 \equiv 5 \pmod{11^3}$.   **2.** $x^2 \equiv 6 \pmod{11^3}$.   **3.** $x^2 \equiv 2 \pmod{11^2}$.

39. Residues of given order. We now give special attention to the number c in the congruence $x^n \equiv c \pmod{q}$, q being any number which has primitive roots, and n fixed.

THEOREM 27. *The necessary and sufficient condition that the congruence* (1) $x^n \equiv c$ *(mod q) shall be solvable is that* (2) $c^{\phi/d} \equiv 1$ *(mod q), where* $\phi = \phi(q)$ *and* $d = (n, \phi)$.

Now (1) is equivalent to $n \operatorname{ind} x \equiv \operatorname{ind} c \pmod{\phi}$.

The condition is necessary, for if (1) is solvable, then $\operatorname{ind} c = rd$. That is, $c \equiv g^{rd}$, where g is a primitive root of q. Then $c^{\phi/d} \equiv g^{rd\phi/d} \equiv g^{r\phi} \equiv 1 \pmod{q}$.

The condition is also sufficient, for assume that $c^{\phi/d} \equiv 1 \pmod{q}$ and let $c \equiv g^i$. Then $c^{\phi/d} \equiv g^{i\phi/d} \equiv 1$. Hence i ($= \operatorname{ind} c$) is a multiple of d and therefore (1) is solvable.

When $x^n \equiv c \pmod{q}$ has a solution, c is said to be a *power residue of* q *of the* nth *order, and otherwise a non-residue.* Then c is an *n*ic residue or non-residue of q according as $c^{\phi/d} \equiv 1 \pmod{q}$ or not. This is known as *Euler's Criterion.* Now, since $\dfrac{\phi}{d}$ is a divisor of ϕ, (2) has just $\dfrac{\phi}{d}$ solutions, and we state:

THEOREM 28. *The number of incongruent residues of the* nth *order modulo* q *is* $\dfrac{\phi}{d}$ *, and these residues are the roots of the congruence* $x^{\phi/d} \equiv 1$ *(mod q).*

Example (a). For what values of c can $x^2 \equiv c \pmod{7}$ be solved; that is, what are the quadratic (second-order) residues of 7? Here $n = 2$, $\phi = 6$, $d = (2, 6) = 2$, and $\dfrac{\phi}{d} = \dfrac{6}{2} = 3$. Then there are three quadratic residues of 7, and they are the roots of the congruence $c^3 \equiv 1 \pmod{7}$. These are 1, 2, and 4.

Example (b). For what values of c can $x^3 \equiv c \pmod{49}$ be solved? $n = 3$, $\phi = 42$, $d = (3, 42) = 3$, $\dfrac{\phi}{d} = 14$. Then $c^{14} \equiv 1 \pmod{49}$. Since 3 is a primitive root of 49 (see Exercise 7, page

69), we have $c \equiv 3^3, 3^6, 3^9, \cdots, 3^{3i}, \cdots, 3^{42}$, which reduce modulo 49 to 27, −6, −15, · · ·, 1 respectively.

Example (c). For what values of c can $x^5 \equiv c$ (mod 49) be solved? $n = 5, \phi = 42, d = 1, \dfrac{\phi}{d} = 42$. Then $c^{42} \equiv 1$ (mod 49). Hence c may be any integer prime to 49.

EXERCISES XII

1. Find the cubic residues of 7.

2. Find the quadratic residues of 11.

3. Find the 7th order residues of 29. Check by the table of power residues modulo 29.

4. Find the 9th order residues of 54.

5. For what primes p is every number $<p$ a cubic residue? What can you say about the cubic residues of other odd primes?

6. Show that any odd prime p has just $\dfrac{p-1}{2}$ quadratic residues (two solutions).

7. Prove that if the congruence $x^n \equiv 1$ (mod p) has n roots then n is a divisor of $p - 1$ (a converse of Theorem 20).

Chapter IV

QUADRATIC RESIDUES

40. Quadratic character. In the study of quadratic residues we shall meet some of the most beautiful results in the whole field of number theory. If in Theorem 28 of the last chapter the modulus is an odd prime p, and $n = 2$, the theorem states that there are just $\dfrac{p-1}{2}$ quadratic residues, and hence also $\dfrac{p-1}{2}$ quadratic non-residues, of p. By the preceding theorem we see that an integer c (prime to p) is a quadratic residue or non-residue of p according as $c^{\frac{p-1}{2}} \equiv 1 \pmod p$ or $c^{\frac{p-1}{2}} \not\equiv 1 \pmod p$. But since for all values of c we have

$$c^{p-1} \equiv 1 \pmod p, \quad \text{that is,} \quad (c^{\frac{p-1}{2}} - 1)(c^{\frac{p-1}{2}} + 1) \equiv 0 \pmod p$$

it follows that

$$c^{\frac{p-1}{2}} \equiv 1 \quad \text{or} \quad -1 \pmod p$$

Hence $c^{\frac{p-1}{2}} \equiv -1 \pmod p$ is the necessary and sufficient condition that c be a quadratic non-residue of p. The reader should verify these statements from the tables of power residues.

The case of an odd composite modulus m reduces immediately to that of the prime modulus because of Theorem 17, page 57, and Theorem 26, page 71, which taken together imply that *c is a residue of odd* m *if and only if* c *is a residue of every prime factor of* m. In our further discussions, when it can be done without ambiguity, we shall use the terms residue and non-residue as meaning quadratic residue and quadratic non-residue, and assume that p represents an odd prime, unless otherwise described. The relationship of an integer c to p, as to whether it is a residue or non-residue of p, will be referred to as its quadratic character with respect to p and will be symbolized by $(c \mid p) = 1$ or -1, respectively. That is, $(6 \mid 19) = 1$ means that 6 is a residue of 19, and $(13 \mid 19) = -1$ means that 13 is a non-residue of 19. This symbolic statement of quadratic character is due to Legendre.

Let c_1 and c_2 be any two integers prime to p. Then

$$(c_1 \cdot c_2)^{\frac{p-1}{2}} \equiv c_1^{\frac{p-1}{2}} \cdot c_2^{\frac{p-1}{2}} \equiv 1 \quad \text{or} \quad -1 \ (\text{mod } p)$$

according as c_1 and c_2 are alike or unlike in their quadratic character with respect to p. Hence we may state

THEOREM 1. *The product of two residues or of two non-residues is a residue, and the product of a residue and a non-residue is a non-residue; or in symbols* $(a|p) \ (b|p) = (ab|p)$.

EXERCISES I

1. Show that -1 is a residue or a non-residue of p according as $p = 4n + 1$ or $4n - 1$ [that is, $(-1 \mid p) = (-1)^{\frac{p-1}{2}}$].

2. Prove that -3 is a residue of $p = 3n + 1$ and a non-residue of $p = 3n - 1$. *Suggestion:* Use Theorem 20, Chapter III, and its converse with the congruence $x^3 - 1 \equiv (x - 1) (x^2 + x + 1) \equiv 0 \ (\text{mod } p)$

3. Find the primes $p = 12n \pm a$, where $0 < a < 6$, of which 3 is a residue.

4. Determine the values of c for which $(c|13) = 1$.

5. Justify the congruence $(c|p) \equiv c^{\frac{p-1}{2}} \ (\text{mod } p)$.

Evaluate:

6. $(3|31) \ (-1|31), \quad (60|61) \ (58|61)$.

7. $(2|11) \ (5|11), \quad (30|13) \ (12|13)$.

Evaluate with the aid of tables of power residues:

8. $(11|19) \ (13|19) \ (5|19), \ (1320|19)$. **9.** $(198|29), \ (650|29)$.

10. Determine the quadratic residues of q in terms of one of its primitive roots, where q is any number having primitive roots.

41. The quadratic reciprocity law. We now seek to develop a more efficient method of determining the value of $(c|p)$. Resolving into prime factors, we have $c = \pm \ 2^{\alpha_0} \cdot p_1^{\alpha_1} \cdot p_2^{\alpha_2} \cdots p_k^{\alpha_k}$, where the p_i are odd primes. By Theorem 1 the value of $(c|p)$ is known once we know the values of $(-1|p)$, $(2|p)$, $(p_i|p)$. In passing we note that we may, again by virtue of Theorem 1, replace each odd α_i by 1, and each even α_i by 0, without changing $(c|p)$. The value of $(-1|p)$ is already known from Exercise 1 above. To evaluate $(p_i|p)$ we employ the beautiful quadratic reciprocity law, which sets up a surprising relation between $(q|p)$ and $(p|q)$ where p and q are odd primes. The law was discovered by Legendre, but was first proved by Gauss, who gave six different proofs for it. Gauss called this law "the gem of the higher arithmetic." We shall follow Gauss's third proof, also obtaining in the course of the argument the value of $(2|p)$.   The first step is to prove

THEOREM 2 (*The Lemma of Gauss*).   *If* q *is any positive integer not divisible by the odd prime* p, *and if* n *denotes the number of least positive residues modulo* p *of the numbers*

$$(1) \qquad\qquad q, 2q, 3q, \cdots, \tfrac{1}{2}(p-1)q$$

which exceed $\dfrac{p}{2}$, *then*

$$(2) \qquad\qquad (q|p) = (-1)^n$$

Obviously all numbers (1) are different from zero modulo p, and, as in Theorem 9, Chapter III, no two of them are congruent modulo p.

Let $a_1, a_2, \cdots, a_n$ be the residues of (1) $> \dfrac{p}{2}$, and $b_1, b_2, \cdots, b_k$ $[k = \tfrac{1}{2}(p-1) - n]$ those which are $< \dfrac{p}{2}$.

Then the numbers $p - a_i$ are each > 0 and $< \dfrac{p}{2}$, and also they are all different from the b_j.   For if $p - a_i = b_j$, then $p = a_i + b_j \equiv \alpha q + \beta q = (\alpha + \beta)q$.   But this is not true since $(q, p) = 1$ and α and β are each $< \dfrac{p}{2}$.

Hence the $h = \tfrac{1}{2}(p-1)$ numbers

$$(3) \qquad p - a_1, p - a_2, \cdots, p - a_n, b_1, b_2, \cdots, b_k$$

are the h positive integers $< \dfrac{p}{2}$.   Therefore

$$\prod_1^n (p - a_i) \cdot \prod_1^k b_j = [\tfrac{1}{2}(p-1)]! = h!$$

But $\qquad \prod_1^n (p - a_i) \cdot \prod_1^k b_j \equiv (-1)^n \prod_1^n a_i \prod_1^k b_j \pmod{p}$

And by (1)

$$(-1)^n \prod_1^n a_i \prod_1^k b_j \equiv (-1)^n q^h \cdot h! \pmod{p}$$

Combining these results we have

$$(-1)^n q^h \cdot h! \equiv h! \pmod{p}$$

or $\qquad\qquad\qquad (-1)^n q^h \equiv 1 \pmod{p}$

and multiplying through by $(-1)^n$

$$q^h \equiv (-1)^n \pmod{p}$$

Hence by Exercise 5 above

(4) $(q|p) = (-1)^n$

We recall that in this result q is any positive integer.

Exercise. Take $q = 11$, $p = 19$, form the numbers used in the above argument, and check the result.

The next step in the argument is to show that, when q is odd

$(q|p) = (-1)^M$, where $M = \displaystyle\sum_{i=1}^{h} \left[\frac{iq}{p}\right]$ and the symbol $\left[\dfrac{iq}{p}\right]$ means,

as in Chapter I, the greatest integer in the quotient $\dfrac{iq}{p}$.

Since $iq = p\left[\dfrac{iq}{p}\right] + r_i$, where r_i is the least positive residue of iq modulo p, we have

$$\sum_{1}^{h} iq = \sum_{1}^{h} p \cdot \left[\frac{iq}{p}\right] + \sum_{1}^{h} r_i$$

or

$$q\sum_{1}^{h} i = p \sum_{1}^{h} \left[\frac{iq}{p}\right] + \sum_{1}^{n} a_i + \sum_{1}^{k} b_i$$

But

$$\sum_{1}^{h} i = 1 + 2 + \cdots + \frac{p-1}{2} = \frac{p^2-1}{8}$$

Then putting $\quad \dfrac{p^2-1}{8} = P, \quad \displaystyle\sum_{1}^{n} a_i = A, \quad \sum_{1}^{k} b_i = B$

we have $qP = pM + A + B$

Also adding the numbers (3) we have

$$P = np - A + B$$

By subtraction

(5) $P(q-1) = p(M-n) + 2A$

Now, assuming q to be odd, it follows that $M - n$ is even or $M \equiv n \pmod{2}$. Hence from (4) we have

(6) $(q|p) = (-1)^M$

Now, if we assume q to be an odd prime, p and q can be interchanged in the foregoing argument with the result that

(7) $$(p|q) = (-1)^N$$

where $$N = \sum_{1}^{l} \left[\frac{ip}{q} \right] \quad \text{and} \quad l = \frac{q-1}{2}$$.

Then multiplying the corresponding members of (6) and (7) we have

(8) $$(p|q)\,(q|p) = (-1)^{M+N}$$

Our next step then is to show that

$$M + N = h \cdot l = \frac{p-1}{2} \cdot \frac{q-1}{2}$$

We are led to this result by the following computation of the value of M, in which we assume $q < p$ without loss of generality. Recall that by definition

$$M = \left[\frac{q}{p} \right] + \left[\frac{2q}{p} \right] + \cdots + \left[\frac{iq}{p} \right] + \cdots + \left[\frac{hq}{p} \right].$$

Since $q < p$, the first term in this series of integers is zero and each term is either equal to the preceding or is one unit greater. We first find the value of i such that

$$\left[\frac{iq}{p} \right] = t - 1 \quad \text{and} \quad \left[\frac{(i+1)q}{p} \right] = t$$

Since $i + 1 < p$ and $q < p$, neither of these fractions is an integer. Then

$$\frac{iq}{p} < t < \frac{(i+1)q}{p}$$

or $$i < \frac{tp}{q} < i + 1$$

Hence $i = \left[\dfrac{tp}{q} \right]$ is the number of the last term having the value $t - 1$. Likewise $\left[\dfrac{(t-1)p}{q} \right]$ is the number of the last term having the value $t - 2$. Then $\left[\dfrac{tp}{q} \right] - \left[\dfrac{(t-1)p}{q} \right]$ is the number of terms having the value $t - 1$. In this way M may be shown as the sum of the products of each integer occurring in the series by the number of times it occurs. The last term of the series is $\left[\dfrac{hq}{p}\right]$. Putting in the value of h and noting that $p - q < 2p$,

$$\left[\frac{\frac{1}{2}(p - 1)q}{p}\right] = \left[\frac{pq - p + p - q}{2p}\right] = \left[\frac{q - 1}{2} + \frac{p - q}{2p}\right] = \frac{q - 1}{2} = l$$

The number of the last term having the value $l - 1$ is $i = \left[\dfrac{lp}{q}\right]$. Thus there are $h - \left[\dfrac{lp}{q}\right]$ terms at the end of the series each having the value l. Hence

$$M = 0 \cdot \left\{\left[\frac{p}{q}\right] - \left[\frac{0 \cdot p}{q}\right]\right\} + 1 \cdot \left\{\left[\frac{2p}{q}\right] - \left[\frac{p}{q}\right]\right\} + 2 \cdot \left\{\left[\frac{3p}{q}\right] - \left[\frac{2p}{q}\right]\right\}$$

$$+ \cdots + (l - 1) \left\{\left[\frac{lp}{q}\right] - \left[\frac{(l - 1)p}{q}\right]\right\} + l \cdot \left\{h - \left[\frac{lp}{q}\right]\right\}$$

$$= -\left[\frac{p}{q}\right] - \left[\frac{2p}{q}\right] - \left[\frac{3p}{q}\right] - \cdots - \left[\frac{lp}{q}\right] + hl$$

$$= -N + hl$$

Or $M + N = hl$, and putting this result in (8) we can state the quadratic reciprocity law:

THEOREM 3. *If* p *and* q *are distinct odd primes* (p|q) (q|p) $=$ $(-1)^{hl}$, *where* h $= \dfrac{p - 1}{2}$, *and* l $= \dfrac{q - 1}{2}$.

We note that h and l are even or odd according as the corresponding primes p and q are of the form $4n + 1$ or $4n - 1$. If either is even, the product of the Legendre symbols is $+1$. That is, *if either* p *or* q *is of the form* 4n $+ 1$, (p|q) $=$ (q|p); *but, if both are of the form* 4n $- 1$, (p|q) $= -$ (q|p).

The importance of these results in determining the quadratic character of one odd prime with respect to another is readily seen. For example, to determine whether 5 is a residue of 3 we write $(5|31) = (31|5)$ since 5 is of the form $4n + 1$. In the latter symbol 5 is the modulus. Hence $(31|5) = (1|5) = 1$. Or to determine the quadratic character of 31 with respect to 83, $(31|83) = - (83|31) = - (21|31) = - (3|31) (7|31) = - (1|3) (3|7) = - (+1) (-1) = +1.$

It remains for us to find a method of determining the quadratic character of the even prime 2 with respect to an odd prime. When $q = 2$, (4) becomes $(2|p) = (-1)^n$. Also $M = 0$ and (5) becomes $P = - pn + 2A$. Hence $P \equiv n \pmod 2$, and $(2|p) = (-1)^P$, where $P = \dfrac{p^2 - 1}{8}$.

EXERCISES II

1. Show that 2 is a residue of all primes of the form $8n \pm 1$ and a non-residue of all others.

Determine the following quadratic characters:

2. $(15|67)$.   **3.** $(22|101)$.   **4.** $(182|271)$.   **5.** $(969|1013)$.

6. If $12n + b$ is a prime, use the reciprocity law to find for what values of b $(3|12n + b) = (12n + b|3) = (b|3)$. Similarly, for what values of b is $(3|12n + b) = - (12n + b|3) = - (b|3)$? Thus determine which forms $12n + b$ represent primes having 3 as a residue, and which represent primes having 3 as a non-residue.

7. Determine values of b so that the forms $10n + b$ will represent all primes of which 5 is a residue.

8. Determine values of b so that the forms $44n + b$ will represent all primes of which 11 is a residue.

9. Determine values of b so that the forms $20n + b$ will represent all primes of which -5 is a residue.

10. Show that the product of the quadratic residues of a prime p is $\equiv 1$ or -1 modulo p according as $p = 4n - 1$ or $4n + 1$. *Suggestion:* Recall that the even powers of a primitive root of p are the residues of p.

11. If p is a prime $4n - 1$, and if m is the number of positive quadratic non-residues $< \dfrac{p}{2}$, then $[\frac{1}{2}(p - 1)]! \equiv (-1)^m \pmod p$

12. Show that any quadratic residue of an odd prime p is a quadratic residue of p^n.

13. Consider the graph of the line $y = \dfrac{q}{p} x$, and the rectangle formed by the lines $x = 0$, $y = 0$, $x = \dfrac{p}{2}$, and $y = \dfrac{q}{2}$, of which $y = \dfrac{q}{p} x$ is a diagonal. By counting the points within the rectangle whose coordinates are integers, show that

$$M + N = \frac{p - 1}{2} \cdot \frac{q - 1}{2}$$

42. Jacobi symbol. In the Legendre symbol the modulus is an odd prime, which is a necessary condition for the symbol to be interpreted as quadratic character. We now introduce the Jacobi symbol, which has the same form, but in which the modulus may be composite. Consequently when the modulus is composite this symbol is not to be interpreted simply as quadratic character, although at times it is identical with the Legendre symbol.

Let P be any positive odd integer. Then either $P = 1$ or $P = \prod_1^k p_i$, where the p_i are odd primes not necessarily distinct. Let n be any integer prime to P. Then we define

$$(9) \qquad (n|1) = 1, \quad \text{and} \quad (n|P) = (n|p_1)\,(n|p_2) \cdots (n|p_k)$$

That this should not be interpreted simply as quadratic character is evident when we note that if an even number of the symbols $(n|p_i)$ were negative their product would be positive, whereas if n were a residue of P it would necessarily be a residue of each p_i and all symbols $(n|p_i)$ would be positive. So, when the Jacobi symbol has the value $+1$, n is not necessarily a quadratic residue of P. But when the Jacobi symbol has the value -1, n must be a non-residue of P.

THEOREM 4. *If* n *is relatively prime to the positive odd integers* P *and* Q *then*

$$(10) \qquad\qquad (n|P)\,(n|Q) = (n|PQ)$$

This follows at once from (9) if we put $P = \prod_1^k p_i$ and $Q = \prod_1^l q_i$. For

$$(n|PQ) = (n|p_1) \cdots (n|p_k)\,(n|q_1) \cdots (n|q_l)$$

$$= (n|P)\,(n|Q)$$

THEOREM 5. *If* m *and* n *are each prime to the positive odd integer* P, *then*

$$(11) \qquad\qquad (m|P)\,(n|P) = (mn|P)$$

For by (9)

$$(m|P)\,(n|P) = (m|p_1) \cdots (m|p_k)\,(n|p_1) \cdots (n|p_k)$$

Then by Theorem 1 (since these moduli are odd primes the symbols are also of the Legendre type) this product becomes

$$(mn|p_1) \cdots (mn|p_k) = (mn|P)$$

THEOREM 6. *If* n *is prime to the positive odd integer* P, *and if* n $\equiv$ m *(mod* P), *then*

(12) $$(n|P) = (m|P)$$

For, since $n \equiv m$ (mod P), we have $n \equiv m$ (mod p_i) for all values of i. Then by definition of the Legendre symbol

$$(n|p_i) = (m|p_i)$$

Hence we can write

$$(n|P) = (n|p_1) \cdots (n|p_k) = (m|p_1) \cdots (m|p_k) = (m|P)$$

THEOREM 7. *If* P *is a positive odd integer*,

(13) $$(-1|P) = (-1)^{\frac{1}{2}(P-1)}$$

By definition $(-1|P) = \prod_1^k (-1|p_i)$, which by Exercises I, 1,

$$= (-1)^{\sum_1^k \frac{1}{2}(p_i-1)}$$

Now we may write $P = \prod_1^k p_i = \prod_1^k [1 + (p_i - 1)]$. And when this product is expanded all the terms except $1 + \sum_1^k (p_i - 1)$ are multiples of 4. Hence

$$P \equiv 1 + \sum_1^k (p_i - 1) \ (\text{mod } 4)$$

or

$$P - 1 \equiv \sum_1^k (p_i - 1) \ (\text{mod } 4)$$

and

$$\tfrac{1}{2}(P - 1) \equiv \sum_1^k \tfrac{1}{2}(p_i - 1) \ (\text{mod } 2)$$

Then using this result in the above we have

$$(-1|P) = (-1)^{\sum_1^k \frac{1}{2}(p_i-1)} = (-1)^{\frac{1}{2}(P-1)}$$

THEOREM 8. *If* P *is a positive odd integer,*

$$(14) \qquad (2|P) = (-1)^{\frac{1}{8}(P^2-1)}$$

By the paragraph preceding Exercises II, $(2|p) = (-1)^{\frac{1}{8}(p^2-1)}$ when p is an odd prime. Hence

$$(2|P) = \prod_1^k (2|p_i) = (-1)^{\sum\limits_1^k \frac{1}{8}(p_i^2-1)}$$

We may write

$$P^2 = \prod_1^k p_i^2 = \prod_1^k [1 + (p_i^2 - 1)]$$

Since $p_i^2 - 1 \equiv 0 \pmod 8$, when this product is expanded all terms containing as many as two of the factors $p_i^2 - 1$ will be multiples of 64. Hence we have

$$P^2 \equiv 1 + \sum_1^k (p_i^2-1) \pmod{64}$$

or $\qquad \frac{1}{8}(P^2 - 1) \equiv \sum\limits_1^k \frac{1}{8}(p_i^2-1) \pmod 8$

Then using this in the above, we have

$$(2|P) = (-1)^{\sum\limits_1^k \frac{1}{8}(p_i^2-1)} = (-1)^{\frac{1}{8}(P^2-1)}$$

THEOREM 9. *If* P *and* Q *are positive, odd, and relatively prime integers, then*

$$(15) \qquad (P|Q)(Q|P) = (-1)^{\frac{1}{2}(P-1)\cdot\frac{1}{2}(Q-1)}$$

By definition of Jacobi's symbol

$$(P|Q)(Q|P) = \prod_1^l (P|q_j) \cdot \prod_1^k (Q|p_i)$$

Then by Theorem 1 this can be written

$$\Pi \, (p_i|q_j)\cdot\Pi \, (q_j|p_i) \quad \text{or} \quad \Pi \, (p_i|q_j)(q_j|p_i)$$

in which each product is taken for $i = 1, 2, \cdots, k$ and for $j = 1, 2, \cdots, l$.

But by Theorem 3

$$\Pi \ (p_i|q_j) \ (q_j|p_i) \ = \ (-1)^{\sum\limits_{i=1}^{k}\sum\limits_{j=1}^{l}\frac{1}{2}(p_i-1)\cdot\frac{1}{2}(q_j-1)}$$

$$= \ (-1)^{\sum\limits_{1}^{k}\frac{1}{2}(p_i-1)\cdot\sum\limits_{1}^{l}\frac{1}{2}(q_j-1)}$$

and, as shown in the argument for Theorem 7, this exponent is $\equiv \frac{1}{2}(P-1)\cdot\frac{1}{2}(Q-1)$ (mod 2). Therefore

$$(P|Q) \ (Q|P) \ = \ (-1)^{\frac{1}{2}(P-1)\cdot\frac{1}{2}(Q-1)}$$

We now note that the statements of Theorems 5 to 9 inclusive are identical in form with the corresponding statements involving Legendre's symbol. That is, the two kinds of symbols are identical in form, and the laws of operation with them are the same. We may therefore regard the Jacobi symbol and its operations as an algorithm by means of which the positive or negative character of a given symbol is computed. Then, if the first symbol in a chain of operations is also a Legendre symbol, the result may be interpreted as quadratic character.

We illustrate by finding the positive or negative character of $(365|1847)$.

$$(365|1847) \ = \ (1847|365) \ = \ (22|365) \ = \ (2|365) \ (11|365)$$

$$= \ -1\cdot(365|11) \ = \ - \ 1\cdot(2|11) \ = \ - \ 1\cdot-1 \ = \ 1$$

The reader should note the justification for each step taken. The given symbol then has the value $+1$. Since 1847 is a prime this may be stated in terms of quadratic character, although Jacobi symbols were used in the course of the computation. That is, 365 is a quadratic residue of 1847.

EXERCISES III

Evaluate both with and without the use of Jacobi symbols (the moduli are primes):

1. $(195|1901)$.   **2.** $(182|1831)$.

3. Show that $(6|P) = 1$ if $P \equiv \pm1$, or ±5 (mod 24), and $= -1$ if $P \equiv \pm7$, or ±11 (mod 24).

4. If P and Q are as given in Theorem 9, and $2P > Q$, show that

$$(\pm \ P|Q) \ = \ (-1)^{\frac{1}{2}(P-1)}\cdot(\pm P|2P-Q)$$

43. General quadratic congruence. The general congruence of the second degree in one variable may be written

$$ax^2 + bx + c \equiv 0 \ (\text{mod } m)$$

in which m is composite. By Chapter III its solution may be made to depend upon the solution of a system of congruences with prime moduli. Hence we shall confine our discussion to the congruence

$$(1) \qquad ax^2 + bx + c \equiv 0 \ (\text{mod } p)$$

where p is an odd prime and does not divide a. If 2 is the modulus, the solutions (when they exist) are readily found by inspection.

If $a \not\equiv 1 \ (\text{mod } p)$ we multiply through the congruence by α where $a\alpha \equiv 1 \ (\text{mod } p)$, getting

$$(2) \qquad x^2 + b\alpha x + c\alpha \equiv 0 \ (\text{mod } p)$$

When $b\alpha$ is even we complete the square of the left member by writing

$$(3) \qquad \left(x + \frac{b\alpha}{2}\right)^2 \equiv \frac{b^2\alpha^2}{4} - c\alpha$$

In general, (3) has two roots or none according as $\dfrac{b^2\alpha^2}{4} - c\alpha$ is or is not a quadratic residue of p. However, if $\dfrac{b^2\alpha^2}{4} - c\alpha \equiv 0$ (mod p), (3) becomes

$$\left(x + \frac{b\alpha}{2}\right)^2 \equiv 0 \ (\text{mod } p)$$

which has just the one root $x \equiv -\dfrac{b\alpha}{2}$.

If $b\alpha$ in (2) is odd it may be made even by adding to it either p or $-p$.

Example 1. Solve $5x^2 - 15x + 14 \equiv 0 \ (\text{mod } 17)$.

$$5\alpha \equiv 1 \ \ \text{if} \ \ \alpha \equiv 7$$

Then $\qquad\qquad\qquad x^2 + 14x - 4 \equiv 0$

or $\qquad\qquad\qquad\qquad (x + 7)^2 \equiv 2$, which is a residue of 17

We find $\qquad\qquad\qquad x + 7 \equiv \pm\, 6$

and $\qquad\qquad\qquad\qquad x \equiv -\, 1 \ \ \text{or} \ \ 4$

Example 2.   Solve $7x^2 + 5x - 10 \equiv 0 \pmod{29}$.

If $$7\alpha \equiv 1, \quad \alpha \equiv -4$$

Then $$x^2 - 20x + 11 \equiv 0$$

or $$(x - 10)^2 \equiv 2$$

But $(2|29) = -1$, and no solution exists.

EXERCISES IV

Find all the solutions of:

1. $5x^2 - 11x - 12 \equiv 0 \pmod{161}$.   3. $x^2 + 29x - 40 \equiv 0 \pmod{91}$.

2. $x^2 + x + 1 \equiv 0 \pmod{38}$.   4. $40x^2 + 27x - 2 \equiv 0 \pmod{143}$.

44. Factoring by means of residues. The use of quadratic residues as an aid in factoring numbers depends directly upon the fact that if R is a quadratic residue of m then it is also a residue of each of the prime factors of m. Then, if we know that R is a residue of m, and know also the linear forms for the primes of which R can be a residue, we know linear forms to which the prime factors of m belong.

For example, if we have given that 3 and 5 are quadratic residues of 4189, and recall that primes having 3 as a residue belong to the forms $12n \pm 1$, and those having 5 as a residue belong to the forms $10n \pm 1$, we know that any prime factors which 4189 may have belong to both sets of forms. The primes $< \sqrt{4189}$ satisfying this condition are 11, 59, and 61. By trial, 59 is found to be a factor of 4189, and $4189 = 59 \cdot 71$.

This presupposes that we are able to find residues of the number to be factored. For this purpose we recall the equation $Q_{n+1} = \dfrac{D - P_{n+1}^2}{Q_n}$ from the bottom of page 31. Writing this in the form $P_{n+1}^2 = D - Q_n Q_{n+1}$ we see that $-Q_n Q_{n+1}$ is a quadratic residue of D. Then if $\sqrt{D}$ is expanded into a continued fraction, $-Q_1 Q_2 = -Q_2$ is a residue of D (since $Q_1 = 1$). Since $-Q_2 Q_3$ is also a residue, Q_3 is a residue. Continuing this with each successive $Q_n Q_{n+1}$ we secure, as residues of D, $-Q_4, Q_5$, and in general $-Q_{2i}$, and Q_{2i+1}.

To illustrate we find residues of 4189 factored above. The

expansion of $\sqrt{4189}$ gives the following elements of the continued fraction:

i	1	2	3	4	5	6	7	8	9 $\cdots$
P_i	0	64	29	43	22	35	17	58	63 $\cdots$
Q_i	1	93	36	65	57	52	75	11	20 $\cdots$
a_i	64	1	2	1	1	1	1	11	6 $\cdots$

From these values of Q_i, residues are found. 5 is a residue from $Q_9 = 20$, 3 from $Q_7 = 75$, -11 from $Q_8 = 11$, etc.

The usefulness of this method of factoring numbers obviously depends upon knowing the forms of primes of which given numbers are residues. Or better yet would be a list of such primes instead of the forms to which they belong. Such lists have been prepared by D. N. Lehmer and published by the Carnegie Institution in the form of factor stencils. The stencils are sheets of paper on each of which are listed all primes $\leq 47,493$. Then for a given residue R (containing no square factor) a sheet is prepared to show the primes of which R is a residue by punching holes at the positions occupied by such primes. These sheets are prepared for both the positive and negative residues for values of R up to 238. Then, when a few residues of a number D are known, their stencils are superimposed upon each other. Primes having all these residues will be revealed by holes showing through all the stencils. This gives a list of primes among which any existing prime factors of D will be found.

EXERCISES V

Find the prime factors of:

1. 1633.   **2.** 3337.

Find residues suitable for use with the stencils in factoring:

3. 27,641.   **4.** 226,801.

CHAPTER V

DIOPHANTINE EQUATIONS

Although the study of indeterminate equations and their solution in integers has had a very important place in the development of number theory, there is not a well-unified body of knowledge based upon general methods. We have already solved the equation $ax + by + c = 0$ in integers by means of the Euclidean algorithm, and again by the use of continued fractions. Also incidental to the latter subject the equation $x^2 - Dy^2 = N$ was discussed with particular reference to certain values of N. In this chapter we will not attempt more than a brief introduction to a few of the more common indeterminate equations and methods of solving them in integers.

45. Simultaneous linear equations. The solution of the linear equation in two variables finds direct application in the solution in integers of two simultaneous linear equations in three variables. Such a linear system is

(1)
$$a_1 x + b_1 y + c_1 z + d_1 = 0$$
$$a_2 x + b_2 y + c_2 z + d_2 = 0$$

It is easily seen that even a single equation of this type may have no solution in integers. Such a one is $2x - 10y + 4z + 5 = 0$. For since 2 divides each of the coefficients of x, y, and z it must also divide the constant term if the equation is to be satisfied in integers. Also we may have two equations of this type each of which has solutions in integers but taken simultaneously they have no integral solution. For example,

$$19x + 10y + 7z + 3 = 0$$

$$5x + 2y + 2z + 1 = 0$$

$x = 10$, $y = -20$, $z = 1$ is a solution of the first, and $x = 1$, $y = -4$, $z = 1$ a solution of the second. But no integral solution exists for them taken together. For, eliminating z, we get $3x + 6y - 1 = 0$, which has no solution in integers, as it would necessarily have if the given equations had a common solution.

Eliminating one variable, say z, from (1), we get

$$(a_1c_2 - a_2c_1)x + (b_1c_2 - b_2c_1)y - (c_1d_2 - c_2d_1) = 0$$

which we write more simply as

$$(2) \qquad (ac)x + (bc)y - (cd) = 0$$

In order for (1) to have a solution in integers it is necessary that the g.c.d. of (ac) and (bc) should be a divisor of (cd). This is in addition to the necessary conditions that in each equation of (1) the g.c.d. of the coefficients of x, y, and z must divide the constant term.

Let x_1, y_1, z_1 be a solution in integers of (1). Then these equations may be written

$$(3) \qquad \begin{aligned} a_1(x - x_1) + b_1(y - y_1) + c_1(z - z_1) = 0 \\ a_2(x - x_1) + b_2(y - y_1) + c_2(z - z_1) = 0 \end{aligned}$$

If none of the numbers (bc), (ca), and (ab) is zero, (3) is equivalent to

$$(4) \qquad \frac{x - x_1}{(bc)} = \frac{y - y_1}{(ca)} = \frac{z - z_1}{(ab)}$$

If, for example, $(bc) = 0$, then (4) is replaced by

$$(4') \qquad x - x_1 = 0, \quad \frac{y - y_1}{(ca)} = \frac{z - z_1}{(ab)}$$

If two of the numbers (bc), (ca), and (ab) are zero, then all are zero, and either equations (1) are identical, or they have no common solution.

It is of interest to note that equations (1) are the equations of planes, and that the various steps in the solution may be interpreted geometrically.

Now let the value of the ratios in (4) or (4') be $\dfrac{r}{s}$ where $(r, s) = 1$. Then

$$x = x_1 + (bc)\frac{r}{s}, \quad y = y_1 + (ca)\frac{r}{s}, \quad z = z_1 + (ab)\frac{r}{s}$$

in which x, y, and z are integers when and only when s is a divisor of (bc), (ca), and (ab). Now if g is the g.c.d. of (bc), (ca), and (ab), then $\dfrac{t}{g}$, where t takes all integral values, positive, negative, and zero, represents all possible values of the ratio for which x, y, and z are integers. Moreover, no two values of $\dfrac{t}{g}$ can give the same solution. Hence when a particular solution of (1) is found the general solution may be written

$$x = x_1 + \frac{(bc)t}{g}, \quad y = y_1 + \frac{(ca)t}{g}, \quad z = z_1 + \frac{(ab)t}{g}$$

To illustrate, find the general solution of

$$2x - y + 3z + 10 = 0$$

$$x + y - 5z - 6 = 0$$

Eliminating y by addition, we get

$$3x - 2z + 4 = 0$$

a solution of which is $x = 2$, $z = 5$. Putting these values in either of the first equations we get $y = 29$. We compute

$$(bc) = b_1c_2 - b_2c_1 = 2, \quad (ca) = 13, \quad (ab) = 3$$

Then $g = 1$, and the general solution is

$$x = 2 + 2t, \quad y = 29 + 13t, \quad z = 5 + 3t$$

Solutions in positive integers are obtained for all values of $t > -1$.

EXERCISES I

Find the general solution in integers, where such exists, and determine the number of positive integral solutions for:

1. $x + 3y - 4z - 8 = 0$
$2x + y + 3z - 39 = 0.$

2. $11x + y - 6z = 0$
$-3x + 2y + z - 7 = 0.$

3. $3x + 6y - z + 5 = 0$
$4x + 3y + 7z - 4 = 0.$

4. $x - y + 5z + 1 = 0$
$x + 5y - z + 7 = 0.$

46. The equation $x^2 + y^2 = z^2$. Triples of integers which satisfy the equation

$$(5) \qquad\qquad x^2 + y^2 = z^2$$

and hence may represent the sides of a right triangle, have been of special interest to mathematicians since remote times. Pythagoras proved the existence of infinitely many such sets of integers, and they have continued to be of interest and importance in the theory of numbers since, sometimes being referred to as Pythagorean numbers.

In the discussion of this and certain other Diophantine equations a set of values of the variables satisfying the equation is said to form a primitive solution when the numbers of the set have no common divisor greater than unity.

In seeking a general solution of (5) we first make the restriction that it be primitive. This implies that the three numbers are relatively prime in pairs, for any number which is a divisor of any two of them is necessarily a divisor of the third. Also, recalling that the square of an odd integer is of the form $8n + 1$, we see that both x and y cannot be odd. For, if they were, we would have $z^2 = 8k + 2$, making z^2 even but not divisible by 4, which is impossible. Hence one of x and y is even and the other is odd, and consequently z is odd.

Assume $x = 2a$ and $x^2 = z^2 - y^2 = (z + y)(z - y)$, in which $z + y$ and $z - y$ are both even. Put $z + y = 2u$, $z - y = 2v$. Then $y = u - v$ and $z = u + v$. Also $x^2 = 4a^2 = 4uv$, $a^2 = uv$. Since $(y, z) = 1$, it follows that $(u, v) = 1$. Then we can put $u = m^2$, $v = n^2$, where $(m, n) = 1$. Consequently $x^2 = 4m^2n^2$ and $x = \pm 2mn$, $y = u - v = m^2 - n^2$, and $z = u + v = m^2 + n^2$.

Hence all primitive solutions of (5) are represented by those forms where m and n are relatively prime and one of them is even. And, conversely, since $2m^2 = z + y$, $2n^2 = z - y$, and any common prime divisor of y and z other than 2 would divide both m and n, then any relatively prime integers, m and n, one of them being even, give a primitive solution of (5).

Then all positive integral solutions of (5) may be represented by

$$x = 2kmn, \quad y = k(m^2 - n^2), \quad z = k(m^2 + n^2)$$

in which k is any positive integer and m and n are as described. It is clear that we may also impose the condition that $m > n$.

For any interchange of the values of m and n does not affect the numerical values of x, y, and z, but simply changes the sign of y. Letting $k = 1$, a few of the primitive solutions are

m	n	x	y	z
2	1	4	3	5
3	2	12	5	13
4	1	8	15	17
4	3	24	7	25
5	2	20	21	29
5	4	40	9	41

A second method of finding the Pythagorean numbers, in which we use geometrical concepts, is of interest. Since z cannot be zero, we write equation (5) in the form

$$\frac{x^2}{z^2} + \frac{y^2}{z^2} = 1 \quad \text{and put} \quad \frac{x}{z} = u, \quad \frac{y}{z} = v$$

getting

(6) $$u^2 + v^2 = 1$$

Therefore in order to find integral solutions of (5) we must find rational solutions of (6). Since (6) is the equation of a circle, this is equivalent to finding the rational points, that is, the points with rational coordinates, on the circle. Through the point $P(-1, 0)$ draw a line of slope $\frac{n}{m}$ whose equation will therefore be

(7) $$v = \frac{n}{m}(u + 1)$$

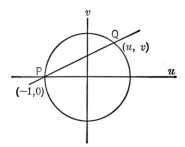

This intersects the circle in a second point $Q(u, v)$. Then it is clear that the slope of the line $\frac{n}{m} = \frac{v}{u+1}$ is rational for any point Q

whose coordinates are rational. And conversely, we will now find u and v to be rational functions of m and n. Eliminating u between (6) and (7), we get

$$m^2v^2 - 2mnv + n^2v^2 = 0$$

from which $v = \dfrac{2mn}{m^2 + n^2}$ for the point Q. Correspondingly, $u = \dfrac{m^2 - n^2}{m^2 + n^2}.$ It follows that whenever the slope of the line is rational the coordinates of Q are rational. Thus a one-to-one correspondence is established between the lines of the pencil P having rational slopes and the rational points on the circle. We note in passing that infinitely many such lines exist within any angular interval about P and consequently infinitely many rational points exist on any interval of the circle.

Now putting $u = \dfrac{x}{z}$ and $v = \dfrac{y}{z}$, we have

$$(8) \qquad \frac{x}{z} = \frac{m^2 - n^2}{m^2 + n^2}, \qquad \frac{y}{z} = \frac{2mn}{m^2 + n^2}$$

Since (8) is thus derived from (5), and also (8) implies (5), as may be seen by squaring and adding the members of (8), it follows that (5) and (8) are equivalent.

We may now write

$$x = \rho(m^2 - n^2)$$

$$y = 2\rho mn$$

$$z = \rho(m^2 + n^2)$$

where ρ is a rational proportionality factor. Put $\rho = \dfrac{k}{d}$, where k and d are integers, and $(k, d) = 1$. Then for x, y, and z to be integers it is necessary that

$$m^2 - n^2 \equiv 0 \;(\mathrm{mod}\; d)$$

and $$m^2 + n^2 \equiv 0 \;(\mathrm{mod}\; d)$$

It follows that $2m^2 \equiv 0 \;(\mathrm{mod}\; d)$, and $2n^2 \equiv 0 \;(\mathrm{mod}\; d)$. But if d divides either m or n, it must divide both, which it cannot do, since $(m, n) = 1$. Hence $2 \equiv 0 \;(\mathrm{mod}\; d)$, and $d = 1$, or 2.

First assume $d = 1$. Then

$$x = k(m^2 - n^2)$$
$$y = 2kmn$$
$$z = k(m^2 + n^2)$$

and for primitive solutions

(9)
$$x = m^2 - n^2$$
$$y = 2mn$$
$$z = m^2 + n^2$$

In (9), m and n are relatively prime and have opposite parity. Conversely, when m and n satisfy these conditions, (9) gives primitive solutions.

We now assume $d = 2$, and have

$$x = \frac{k}{2}(m^2 - n^2)$$
$$y = kmn$$
$$z = \frac{k}{2}(m^2 + n^2)$$

Then for primitive solutions

(10)
$$x = \tfrac{1}{2}(m^2 - n^2)$$
$$y = mn$$
$$z = \tfrac{1}{2}(m^2 + n^2)$$

In (10) it is necessary that m and n have the same parity, and hence they are both odd, since $(m, n) = 1$.

If we now put $m = m' + n'$ and $n = m' - n'$ in (10), we get

$$x = 2m'n'$$
$$y = m'^2 - n'^2$$
$$z = m'^2 + n'^2$$

this is (9) with x and y interchanged. *Hence all primitive solutions of (5) may be obtained from (9).*

EXERCISES II

1. Determine all sets of Pythagorean integers which consist of consecutive terms of an arithmetic progression.

2. Prove that the legs and hypotenuse of all integral right triangles in which the hypotenuse differs from one leg by unity are given by $2n + 1$, $2n^2 + 2n$, $2n^2 + 2n + 1$, n being a positive integer.

3. Prove that the legs and hypotenuse of all integral right triangles in which the hypotenuse differs from one leg by 2, and the three sides are relatively prime, are given by $2n$, $n^2 - 1$, $n^2 + 1$, n being a positive integer.

4. Prove that no set of Pythagorean integers exists in which one integer is the mean proportional between the other two.

5. Prove that there exists no isosceles right triangle whose three sides are integers.

6. Show that the product of the three integers of a Pythagorean set is divisible by 60.

Find formulas for primitive solutions in positive integers of:

7. $x^2 + y^2 = z^4$.   **8.** $x^2 - y^2 = 16z^4$.

9. Find a non-primitive solution of the equation of Exercise 7 such that the values of x and y cannot be obtained from those of a primitive solution by multiplying by a proportionality factor.

10. Do the same for the equation of Exercise 8.

47. The equation $Ax^2 + y^2 = z^2$. We now develop formulas for x, y, and z which satisfy the equation

$$(11) \qquad\qquad Ax^2 + y^2 = z^2$$

in which A is a positive integer with no square factor. The solution is first assumed to be primitive. This is equivalent to requiring that no two of the numbers x, y, and z shall have a common factor. For, obviously, if x and one of the other variables have a common factor greater than unity, then the third variable must contain that factor. Also if $(y, z) = d > 1$, then $Ax^2 = z^2 - y^2$ is divisible by d^2, and since A contains no square factor, d divides x.

Assuming that we have a primitive solution x, y, z we write

$$Ax^2 = z^2 - y^2 = (z + y)(z - y)$$

Since $(y, z) = 1$, the g.c.d. of $z + y$ and $z - y$ is either 2 or 1, according as z and y are both odd, or one is odd and the other even.

First we assume both z and y to be odd and put $z + y = 2u$, $z - y = 2v$, where $(u, v) = 1$. Then $Ax^2 = 4uv$. Since A contains no square factor, x is even, and we write $x = 2a$. Consequently $Ax^2 = 4Aa^2 = 4uv$, and $Aa^2 = uv$. Let m^2 and n^2 be he largest squares in u and v, respectively. Then $u = m^2 r$, $= n^2 s$, where $(m, n) = (r, s) = (r, n) = (s, m) = 1$. Then $4a^2 = m^2 r \cdot n^2 s$, and $A = rs$, $a = mn$. Hence, since $y = u - v$ and $z = u + v$, we have

12) $$x = 2mn, \quad y = rm^2 - sn^2, \quad z = rm^2 + sn^2$$

Thus any primitive solution of (11) in which both y and z are odd can be expressed in terms of r, s, m, and n, where $A = rs$, and m and n are any integers subject to the above conditions, and the added requirement that, if A is odd, m and n have unequal parity.

Conversely, any integers r, s, m, and n satisfying the given conditions give only primitive solutions of this type. For, if $(y, z) > 1$, then $(u, v) > 1$ and some of the given conditions would be contradicted.

We now assume y and z to have unequal parity. As a consequence of this and one of the original assumptions, $z + y$ and $z - y$ are relatively prime. Then, since but one of the terms y^2 and z^2 is even, Ax^2, and consequently A and x, are odd. Put $z + y = u$ and $z - y = v$. Then u and v are odd, $(u, v) = 1$, and $Ax^2 = uv$. Let m^2 and n^2 be the greatest squares in u and v, respectively. We then have $Ax^2 = uv = rm^2 sn^2$, in which $A = rs$, $x = mn$, m and n are both odd, and $(m, n) = (r, s) = (m, s) = (n, r) = 1$. Then

(13) $$x = mn, \quad y = \tfrac{1}{2}(rm^2 - sn^2), \quad z = \tfrac{1}{2}(rm^2 + sn^2)$$

Thus a primitive solution of (11) in which y and z have unlike parity is given by (13) with the accompanying conditions for m, n, r, and s. And, conversely, (13) with these conditions yields only primitive solutions of this type.

The above discussion has been on the basis of whether y and z have the same or unlike parity. However, for the purpose of solving such equations, our results should be stated from the standpoint of whether A is even or odd. Thus summarized these results are:

I. *If in the equation* $Ax^2 + y^2 = z^2$, A *is even and contains no square factor, all primitive solutions and no others are given by* (12).

II. *If in the equation* $Ax^2 + y^2 = z^2$, A *is odd and contains no square factor, all primitive solutions and no others are found by using both* (12) *and* (13).

Obviously all non-primitive solutions are obtained by multiply-ing the primitive solutions by a factor k, which can take any positive integral value.

To illustrate we give a few primitive solutions of:

(a) $6x^2 + y^2 = z^2$. Here A is even and the primitive solutions are obtained from (12), i.e.,

$$x = 2mn, \quad y = rm^2 - sn^2, \quad z = rm^2 + sn^2$$

where $(m, n) = (r, n) = (s, m) = 1, \quad r \cdot s = 6$

r	s	m	n	x	y	z
6	1	1	1	2	5	7
6	1	4	11	88	25	217
2	3	1	3	6	25	29
2	3	5	1	10	47	53

(b) $5x^2 + y^2 = z^2$. Since A is odd, primitive solutions are obtained from both (12) and (13). In using (12) the additional condition that m and n have different parity is imposed, and we get

r	s	m	n	x	y	z
5	1	1	2	4	1	9
5	1	4	3	24	71	89
1	5	4	3	24	29	61
1	5	1	2	4	19	21

From (13), i.e., $x = mn$, $y = \frac{1}{2}(Am^2 - n^2)$, $z = \frac{1}{2}(Am^2 + n^2)$ with m and n both odd, and $(m, n) = (A, n) = 1$, we get

r	s	m	n	x	y	z
5	1	1	1	1	2	3
5	1	5	3	15	58	67
1	5	1	1	1	2	3
1	5	5	3	15	10	35

EXERCISES III

1. Find four solutions of $10x^2 + y^2 = z^2$.

2. Find six solutions (three each with (12) and (13)) of $7x^2 + y^2 = z^2$.

3. Find formulas for x, y, and z which solve the equation $x^2 - y^2 = z^3$.

4. Find two sets of values of x, y, and z which are solutions for the equation in Exercise 3.

48. The equation $ax^2 + bxy + cy^2 = ez^2$. We now develop formulas for the solution in integers of the equation

(14) $$ax^2 + bxy + cy^2 = ez^2$$

in which a, b, c, and e are integers, $e \neq 0$, and $d = b^2 - 4ac$ is not the square of an integer. Such solutions are not always possible. However, if one exists and is known, infinitely many others may be found.

Let $x = j$, $y = k$, $z = l$ be one integral solution where $(j, k, l) = 1$, and they are not all zero. In particular we require that $z \neq 0$, for, if $z = 0$, since d is not a square, no rational values of x and y could satisfy (14). Then dividing through (14) by z we get $a\dfrac{x^2}{z^2} + b\dfrac{x}{z} \cdot \dfrac{y}{z} + c\dfrac{y^2}{z^2} = e$, and, putting $\dfrac{x}{z} = u$ and $\dfrac{y}{z} = v$, we have

$$(15) \qquad\qquad au^2 + buv + cv^2 = e$$

Now a rational solution of (15) may be formed from any integral solution of (14). Conversely an integral solution of (14) may be obtained from any rational solution of (15). For let $u = \dfrac{\alpha}{\beta}$, $v = \dfrac{\gamma}{\delta}$ be a rational solution of (15), α, β, γ, and δ being integers. Then $\dfrac{a\alpha^2}{\beta^2} + \dfrac{b\alpha\gamma}{\beta\delta} + \dfrac{c\gamma^2}{\delta^2} = e$ or $a(\alpha\delta)^2 + b(\alpha\delta)\,(\beta\gamma) + c(\beta\gamma)^2 = e(\beta\delta)^2$ and the integers $\alpha\delta$, $\beta\gamma$, and $\beta\delta$ form a solution of (14). However, even if $\dfrac{\alpha}{\beta}$ and $\dfrac{\gamma}{\delta}$ are in their lowest terms, it is possible that β and δ may have a common divisor >1, and hence this solution of (14) would not be primitive. Therefore there does not exist a one-to-one correspondence between the primitive solutions of (14) and the rational solutions in their lowest terms of (15), analogous to such a one-to-one correspondence for equations (5) and (6).

Since $e \neq 0$, equation (15) represents a proper central conic, and $\left(\dfrac{j}{l}, \dfrac{k}{l}\right)$ are the coordinates of a rational point on it. The rational solutions of (15), which are reduced to their lowest terms, are the coordinates of the rational points of the conic. In finding the rational solutions of (15) we follow the general method used in solving (6). The equation of a line through the point $\left(\dfrac{j}{l}, \dfrac{k}{l}\right)$ with the variable slope $\dfrac{m}{n}$, where m and n are integers not both zero, is $n\left(v - \dfrac{k}{l}\right) = m\left(u - \dfrac{j}{l}\right)$. When $m \neq 0$ and $n \neq 0$, this may

be written $\dfrac{u - j/l}{n} = \dfrac{v - k/l}{m}$. If $m = 0$, then $v - \dfrac{k}{l} = 0$, and

similarly if $n = 0$, $u - \dfrac{j}{l} = 0$. Equating these ratios to w we write

$$(16) \qquad\qquad u = nw + \frac{j}{l}, \quad v = mw + \frac{k}{l}$$

the equations of the line in terms of the parameter w.

By putting the values of u and v from (16) into (15) we get a quadratic equation in w,

$$(an^2 + bmn + cm^2)w^2 + (2anj + bjm + bkn + 2cmk)\frac{w}{l}$$

$$+ \frac{1}{l^2}(aj^2 + bjk + ck^2 - el^2) = 0$$

the constant term of which equals zero. The solution $w = 0$ corresponds to the assumed solution of (15) $u = \dfrac{j}{l}$, $v = \dfrac{k}{l}$. Then

$$w = -\frac{2anj + bjm + bkn + 2cmk}{l(an^2 + bmn + cm^2)}$$

is the second solution. Using this in (16) we get

$$(17) \qquad
\begin{aligned}
u &= \frac{x}{z} = \frac{cjm^2 - 2ckmn - (aj + bk)n^2}{l(an^2 + bmn + cm^2)} \\[2mm]
v &= \frac{y}{z} = \frac{-(bj + ck)m^2 - 2ajmn + akn^2}{l(an^2 + bmn + cm^2)}
\end{aligned}$$

If the two points of intersection of the line and the conic are rational, then the slope of the line is rational and may be expressed by $\dfrac{m}{n}$, where m and n are integers. Then, if x_1, y_1, z_1 is any integral solution of (14), and u_1, v_1 is the rational solution of (15) obtained from it, there exist integers m and n which when substituted in (17) give u_1 and v_1. Conversely, it appears from (17) that, if m and n are integers, u and v are rational, and from them integral solutions of (14) may be obtained. Now we introduce a rational proportionality factor ρ, and write

$$x = \rho[cjm^2 - 2ckmn - (aj + bk)n^2] = \rho r$$

(18) $$y = \rho[-(bj + ck)m^2 - 2ajmn + akn^2] = \rho s$$

$$z = \rho l(cm^2 + bmn + an^2) = \rho t$$

Then, for any integral values of m and n and a value of ρ such that its denominator divides each of r, s, and t, (18) gives integral values of x, y, and z which satisfy (14). And conversely any integral solution of (14) may be obtained from (18) by a suitable choice of integral values of m and n, and a rational ρ.

However, it is not true that by making all possible substitutions of m, n, and ρ we secure each possible integral solution of (14) once and only once. For example, if $(m, n) = g$, then g^2 divides x, y, and z, playing the part of a proportionality factor. Moreover, if we assume $(m, n) = 1$, it is still possible that r, s, and t have a common factor.

In Article 30 of his *Introduction to the Theory of Numbers*, L. E. Dickson sets up a rather complicated set of formulas and conditions, which, when taken with (18), solve equations (14) completely. These define the denominators which should be used for non-integral values of ρ, and give a method of determining the values of m and n to use with each. This is analogous to our discussion above of the value of d in arriving at equations (9) and (10).

By the following example we illustrate the necessity of non-integral values of ρ. Given that one solution of $3x^2 - xy + y^2 = 3z^2$ is 1, 1, 1, find others. Formulas (18) become

$$x = \rho(m^2 - 2mn - 2n^2)$$

$$y = \rho(-6mn + 3n^2)$$

$$z = \rho(m^2 - mn + 3n^2)$$

m	n	ρ	x	y	z	u	v
1	1	1	-3	-3	3	-1	-1
1	1	$\frac{1}{3}$	-1	-1	1	-1	-1
-2	1	1	6	15	9	$\frac{2}{3}$	$\frac{5}{3}$
-2	1	$\frac{1}{3}$	2	5	3	$\frac{2}{3}$	$\frac{5}{3}$
-5	1	1	33	33	33	1	1
-5	1	$\frac{1}{3}$	11	11	11	1	1
-5	1	$\frac{1}{11}$	3	3	3	1	1
-5	1	$\frac{1}{33}$	1	1	1	1	1

From the solving of (15) it follows that there is a one-to-one correspondence between sets of values of u and v, and values of $\frac{m}{n}$, all to be in their lowest terms when non-integral. Hence $m = -2$, $n = 1$ (or $m = 2$, $n = -1$) are the only values of m and n which can give $u = \frac{2}{3}$, $v = \frac{5}{3}$, and consequently there exist no values of m and n from which we can obtain $x = 2$, $y = 5$, $z = 3$ with an integral value of ρ.

EXERCISES IV

Find three solutions of:

1. $2x^2 - xy + y^2 = z^2$, one solution being 1,2,2.

2. $x^2 - 5xy + 18y^2 = 3z^2$, one solution being 2,1,2.

49. The equation $x^n + y^n = z^n$. The famous " Fermat's last theorem " states that the equation

$$(19) \qquad\qquad x^n + y^n = z^n$$

cannot be solved in non-zero integers for n an integer and >2. No proof was left with the statement of the theorem. During the three hundred years since its enunciation attempts to prove the theorem have led to extensive and important developments in the theory of numbers. But all attempts have failed to produce a complete proof. Kummer succeeded in proving it for large classes of numbers. It is known to be true, for example, for all values of $n < 307$, from which it follows that it is true for any value of n having a factor which is less than 307. The significance of the theorem is emphasized by interpreting it in geometrical terms. In order to do this we put $\frac{x}{z} = u$ and $\frac{y}{z} = v$, getting

$$(20) \qquad\qquad u^n + v^n = 1$$

The solving of (19) in integers is equivalent to solving (20) in rational numbers. For $n = 3$ and $n = 4$, (20) represents, respectively, the open and closed curves shown.

Interpreted geometrically the theorem means that the only rational points on the cubic curve are (0, 1) and (1, 0), and the only ones on the quartic are (1, 0), (0, 1), (−1, 0), and (0, −1). Higher odd and even values of n give curves similar in character respectively to these for $n = 3$ and $n = 4$. They all have the remarkable property (within the limits of the truth of the theorem) that their only rational points are their intersections with the coordinate axes.

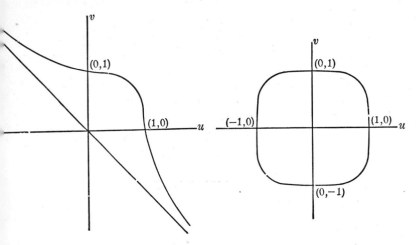

50. Equations having no integral solutions. We will now discuss certain equations which have no solutions in positive integers. First we show that *the equation*

(21)
$$x^4 + y^4 = z^2$$

cannot be solved in integers different from zero.

The method of proof is to assume that solutions exist and show that this leads to a contradiction. Under this assumption let x_1, y_1, z_1 be a solution having the least numerical value of z, and assume $z > 0$.

Note first that $(x_1, y_1) = 1$. For if $(x_1, y_1) = d > 1$, d^4 would divide z_1^2 and $\left(\dfrac{x_1}{d}\right)^4 + \left(\dfrac{y_1}{d}\right)^4 = \left(\dfrac{z_1}{d^2}\right)^2$. Thus we would have a solution of (21) in which $z = \dfrac{z_1}{d^2} < z_1$. But z_1 is the least possible value of $z > 0$ in any solution. Hence $(x_1, y_1) = 1$, and consequently they are not both even. Also x_1 and y_1 cannot both be odd, for then $x_1^4 + y_1^4 \equiv 2 \pmod 4$ while $z_1^2 \equiv 0 \pmod 4$.

We then assume x_1 as even and y_1 odd. Writing the equation in Pythagorean form $(x_1^2)^2 + (y_1^2)^2 = z_1^2$, we can put $x_1^2 = 2mn$, $y_1^2 = m^2 - n^2$, $z_1 = m^2 + n^2$, where $(m, n) = 1$ and one of them is even. If m were even, we would have $y^2 = m^2 - n^2 \equiv -1$ (mod 4), which is impossible. Hence put $n = 2q$, and get $x^2 = 4mq$ or $\left(\dfrac{x}{2}\right)^2 = mq$. Since $(m, q) = 1$, each is a square. Put $m = r^2$ and $q = s^2$, where $(r, s) = 1$, r is odd and >0. Then from $n^2 + y^2 = m^2$ we get $(2s^2)^2 + y^2 = (r^2)^2$. From the solution of this write $2s^2 = 2hk$, and $r^2 = h^2 + k^2$, where $(h, k) = 1$. Then h and k are squares. Put $h = a^2$, $k = b^2$, and we get $r^2 = a^4 + b^4$. But this shows a, b, r to be a solution of (21) in which $0 < r \leqq m < z_1$, whereas z_1 was assumed to be the least positive value of z in any solution. Hence (21) has no integral solution.

We note that this proves the impossibility in non-zero integers of $x^n + y^n = z^n$, where $n \equiv 0$ (mod 4).

EXERCISES V

Show that the following equations are impossible in integers different from zero:

1. $x^4 + 4y^4 = z^2$.

2. $x^4 - y^4 = z^2$. *Suggestion:* $(x^4 + y^4)^2 = z^4 + 4(xy)^4$.

3. $x^4 - y^4 = 2z^2$.

4. $x^4 + 2y^4 = z^2$. *Suggestion:* Start from (12) with $A = 2$.

5. $x^4 - 4y^4 = \pm z^2$.

6. $8x^4 - y^4 = \pm z^2$.

7. $x^4 + y^4 = 2z^2$ (other than $x^2 = y^2 = \pm z$).

8. Prove that the area of an integral right triangle is never equal to twice a square number.

9. Prove that the area of an integral right triangle is never equal to a square number.

10. Prove that the system

$$x^2 + y^2 = z^2, \quad y^2 + z^2 = t^2$$

has no solution in integers all different from zero.

TABLE OF PRIMES

2	179	419	661	947	1229	1523	1823	2131	2437
3	181	421	673	953	231	531	831	137	441
5	191	431	677	967	237	543	847	141	447
7	193	433	683	971	249	549	861	143	459
11	197	439	691	977	259	553	867	153	467
13	199	443	701	983	277	559	871	161	473
17	211	449	709	991	279	567	873	179	477
19	223	457	719	997	283	571	877	203	503
23	227	461	727	1009	289	579	879	207	521
29	229	463	733	013	291	583	889	213	531
31	233	467	739	019	297	597	901	221	539
37	239	479	743	021	301	601	907	237	543
41	241	487	751	031	303	607	913	239	549
43	251	491	757	033	307	609	931	243	551
47	257	499	761	039	319	613	933	251	557
53	263	503	769	049	321	619	949	267	579
59	269	509	773	051	327	621	951	269	591
61	271	521	787	061	361	627	973	273	593
67	277	523	797	063	367	637	979	281	609
71	281	541	809	069	373	657	987	287	617
73	283	547	811	087	381	663	993	293	621
79	293	557	821	091	399	667	997	297	633
83	307	563	823	093	409	669	999	309	647
89	311	569	827	097	423	693	2003	311	657
97	313	571	829	103	427	697	011	333	659
101	317	577	839	109	429	699	017	339	663
103	331	587	853	117	433	709	027	341	671
107	337	593	857	123	439	721	029	347	677
109	347	599	859	129	447	723	039	351	683
113	349	601	863	151	451	733	053	357	687
127	353	607	877	153	453	741	063	371	689
131	359	613	881	163	459	747	069	377	693
137	367	617	883	171	471	753	081	381	699
139	373	619	887	181	481	759	083	383	707
149	379	631	907	187	483	777	087	389	711
151	383	641	911	193	487	783	089	393	713
157	389	643	919	201	489	787	099	399	719
163	397	647	929	213	493	789	111	411	729
167	401	653	937	217	499	801	113	417	731
173	409	659	941	223	511	811	129	423	741

INDEX

(Numbers refer to pages)